As an alternative to other system such as the Freudian—he demonstrates that delusions are most fruitfully studied as condensed and caricatured forms of social language which impart meaning to the patient's experience in relation to, and as a result of, his participation in his culture.

Case studies, written in clear and explicit language, are directly to the point and illuminate the issues in question. The tables at the end of the volume present a statistical evaluation of the psychotic episodes under study. Dr. Weinstein also discusses linguistic structure, institutional identification, family organization, parent-child relationships, symbolic aspects of race and color, sex roles and attitudes, religious and symbolic implications of death and obeah (witchcraft).

The introduction by Dr. David McK. Rioch points out the major contribution of the work to an operational analysis of symbolic behavior.

About the Author

Dr. Edwin A. Weinstein is now dividing his time between research on the relationships of language and stress and the teaching and practise of neurology and psychiatry. He is on the staff of the Walter Reed Army Institute of Research, the National Naval Medical Center, and the Mount Sinai Hospital (New York) and is a Fellow of The William Alanson White Institute of Psychiatry. From 1957 to 1960 he was Psychiatrist for the Government of the Virgin Islands.

CULTURAL ASPECTS
OF DELUSION

Cultural Aspects
of Delusion

A PSYCHIATRIC STUDY OF THE VIRGIN ISLANDS

Edwin A. Weinstein, M.D.

THE FREE PRESS OF GLENCOE, Inc.

A DIVISION OF THE CROWELL-COLLIER PUBLISHING COMPANY

For information, address:

The Free Press of Glencoe, Inc.
A DIVISION OF THE CROWELL-COLLIER PUBLISHING COMPANY
60 Fifth Avenue, New York 11

Library of Congress Catalog Card Number: 62-10593

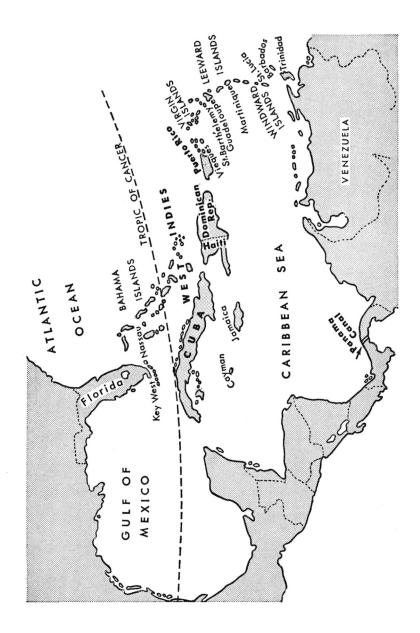

FOREWORD

IN THIS MONOGRAPH Dr. Edwin A. Weinstein presents a combined psychiatric and anthropological approach to the study of delusions, hallucinations, and other communications of patients in psychotic states. The work was conducted chiefly in the Virgin Islands, but includes observations on patients from neighboring groups. The differences among the social mores represented by the different societies studied provided an excellent basis for the analytic method Dr. Weinstein has applied to his problem, and the results reported here represent an important contribution to psychiatric practice and theory.

The analysis of symbolic behavior applied in this work extends into the area of psychotic communication the research that Dr. Weinstein and his associates have conducted through the past twelve years on the symbolic behavior of patients with brain injury. In the earlier investigations it was shown that, apart from focal symptoms —such as hemiplegia, hemianopsia, aphasia, and so forth— diffuse injury or symmetrical brainstem lesions result in changes in the mode or level of symbolic behavior, resulting in language and gesture that may be obscure, but that reveal, nevertheless, *integrated patterns* of response and not merely random loss of parts of functions nor random development of abnormal performances. The detailed studies of brain-injured patients have clearly documented the general thesis that, under the stress of illness, patients are concerned with their immediate life problem and that this concern is communicated in symbols (verbal, gestural, and acted-out) that are part of early learned, preferred systems of intimate human communication. These extensive investigations have also provided strong evidence that, under conditions reducing human capacity for dealing with the complicated data of living, symbolic behavior is more condensed; those symbols are selected that have been learned as more reliable, and they are used as though more concrete (that is, they are used in the sense of what they personally connote rather than what they abstractly denote). In other words, the symbolic behavior is structured selectively according to principles early learned as providing a subjective sense of reality.

In the work presented in this monograph Dr. Weinstein has demonstrated that the same principles apply in the symbolic behavior of patients in psychotic states and that, in terms of this formal type of analysis, the symptoms of disturbed communication are similar in brain injury and in psychosis. It is quite clear, however, that whereas in the great majority of instances the functional deficit is the significant problem in the brain-injured patient's life course, the social context of the major problems of patients in psychotic states varies widely and changes with time.

The importance of these studies for psychiatric practice is the demonstration of a practical method for improving communication between the therapeutic staff and the patient. Instead of discussing the generally accepted— that is, the dictionary—meaning or sense of the symbols, clichés, analogies, and metaphors that the patient uses, attention can be directed to the immediate, frequently very practical, problems that the patient is expressing through the medium of these preferred symbols. To do this successfully, very often a considerable amount of information about the patient's background, his cultural mores, the social situation, and the precipitating events of the psychotic is required. When such information is unavailable, however, knowledge of the principles of reduced levels of symbolic behavior will help to prevent hasty dismissal of obscure communication as "merely psychotic" and also prevent establishing further symbolic distortions by assuming an understanding that cannot be documented.

Dr. Weinstein's studies are no less significant for psychiatric theory and research. Analysis of human communication has attracted increasing attention during the modern period of science, and a wide variety of methods have been applied to the problem, including microlinguistic analysis of vocal behavior, statistical study of word usage, and, most recently, definition of the rules of syntax for use in programming machine translation. Of more practical concern to psychiatrists and social scientists have been studies of semantics and of the formal and informal significance of symbols in social communication. One of the major interests in semantics has been the equivalence of symbols and the principles underlying such equivalent use.

The concept of the equivalence of symbols is old and has been widely held at certain periods—for example, in the religious syncretism of the late Hellenistic and early Roman Empire periods. It is probable that modern interest in this area was aroused mainly by Fraser's interpretation of his monumental collection of reports on religious rites, magic, and myths in *The Golden Bough*. He equated very diverse symbolic systems with symbols acceptable in his own culture, centering around common concerns with the broad areas of family structure, death, birth, and fertility. Freud applied this conceptual operation to the dichotomy between the biological theory of his time and the concurrent humanistic, introspective understanding. He sharpened certain of Fraser's implications quite frankly into "Eros" and "Thanatos" as the general symbolic equivalents of other symbolic communicative forms in the technical language of his system of therapy and equated these with the concepts of sexual and destructive (death) "instincts" as the major "motives" in his psychology.

Since symbols are arbitrary, there is no problem of proof or disproof of their equivalence. The problem is rather that of economy. For the purpose of dealing with a large, heterogeneous human group, a minimum number of highly condensed symbols seems more efficient, especially if a good deal of autonomy is allowed peripherally in interpreting the condensed symbolic system. For research, however, the classification of data on the basis of a few, highly condensed symbols results either in categories that are too inclusive to be useful or else in a cumbersome system of subhypotheses.

A method of analyzing symbolic behavior, very different from systematizing the equivalence of symbols on a conventional or arbitrary basis, was developed by Sapir and later extended by Whorf in the course of comparative anthropological studies of language. The method is essentially a comparative, anthropological study of human communication, correlating the forms and modes of language, gesture, and so forth, and of symbolic value systems with the formal and informal social mores. In the Introduction to this monograph Dr. Weinstein describes the principles of this approach and the general concepts of symbolic behavior that have been derived from its application in anthropological and clinical studies. It is clear that although the equivalence of symbols is arbitrary, the use made of this equivalence is directed by social factors that include both the general mores of the society and the more limited patterns of interaction, modes of verbalization, and expression as well as the symbolic valences preferred by the subject's (or patient's) face-to-face group.

The development of methods for determining such preferences provides the psychiatrist and the social scientist with a research strategy the value of which is only gradually coming to be recognized. For example, one of Dr. Weinstein's most striking findings is that none of the patients from the so-called native population of St. Thomas used "homosexuality" in formulations of delusions, ideas of reference, or other complaints. The sexual mores of this society, as of several others of record, are quite different from those of the majority of Western cultural groups and, consequently, a different symbolic valence is used for communicating those life problems for which sexual symbolic behavior is commonly employed in the continental United States. As a first approximation it appears that in St. Thomas the symbolic valence of choice is *children,* particularly their *care* and *support.* The demonstration of such differences in preferred symbolic behavior between the cultures raises the question whether the "psychodynamics" of the paranoid syndrome are equivalently different in the two cultures or whether there is a common set of psycho-social phenomena differently symbolized. It may well be that the second alternative is a more economic hypothesis and that patients in paranoid states in both cultures are referring to their immediate and inclusive problems in establishing stable, intimate, long-term relations with other persons.

The further development of the Sapir-Whorf hypothesis by its application to neurological and psychiatric patients that Dr. Weinstein has presented is economic—and hence useful for a considerable variety of research purposes. It does not require the postulate of a universal set of qualitatively different, subjective phenomena, characteristic of *Homo sapiens,* which overtly or covertly control all behavior. One can deal instead with intracerebral (neuronal) activity, of which communicative behavior is an integral part, orienting the person—ordinarily referred to as perception and evaluation—and directing the course of his interaction with the environment according to the social mores learned during enculturation. This biological, behavioral approach calls attention to such problems as, for example, the independence of the apparent form of culturally developed patterns of interaction, characteristics of their *course* and the *end-state* at which they arrive. It also calls attention to the contrast between processing information as a *signal* (or "release mechanism") in the course of a well-known pattern of interaction and the *comparison of the information* with a memory standard in less well-known or in novel situations.

Further examples, such as the usefulness of analogies between aspects of human symbolic behavior and the principles of instructions, programs, storage, and so forth now being formulated for computing, decision making and other machines will not be considered here. It is possibly of more importance to call to mind a well-known fact: the development of an operational method requires a great deal of work and detailed testing under a wide variety of conditions. From such a point of view the major contribution of this monograph is that the operational analysis of symbolic behavior, which Dr. Weinstein earlier applied to the study of brain-injured patients, is here shown to be applicable to the symbolic behavior of patients in psychotic states. Many practitioners who have worked intimately with psychotic patients will find here a sound basis in social science theory for clinical observations that previously seemed unique or intuitive. It will thus be possible to communicate and compare data systematically, without the extended training in clinical theory that is now often required.

DAVID McK. RIOCH, M.D.
Director
Division of Neuropsychiatry
Walter Reed Army Institute of Research

PREFACE

THIS STUDY is based on a two-and-one-half-year experience of living and working in the United States Virgin Islands. As the government psychiatrist, I cared for hospitalized psychiatric patients on a twenty-eight-bed wing of a general hospital. Others were seen on an out-patient basis, seeking help privately or by referral from the Department of Social Welfare, law enforcement agencies, and the schools. In the small insular communities of St. Thomas, St. Croix, and St. John almost all patients were personally known to the professional staff, and family histories could be obtained from relatives. Interviews with the parents and guardians of children brought to clinic or seen at the Insular Training Schools for Boys and Girls yielded information on child raising patterns. A seminar held in 1957–1958 with the Department of Welfare on parent-child relationships in the various insular cultures was particularly fruitful. Most of the work was carried on in St. Thomas, with one day a week spent in St. Croix and occasional clinics in St. John and the British Virgin Island of Tortola.

The Virgin Islands were chosen for this study because of the opportunity they offered to observe a number of different cultures living together in a small insular area. An advantage was that the majority group, the native Virgin Islanders, spoke English, while many in the French and Puerto Rican minority groups used English as a second language. My work as a physician gave me a status and provided a framework for relationships. Similarly, living in St. Thomas with my wife and children as a member of the community involved a social participation that might have been lacking had the study been conducted on a more academic basis.

The observations of patients in the Virgin Islands were supplemented by visits to the mental hospitals of Antigua, St. Lucia, Barbados, and Martinique. For the opportunity to interview patients in these islands and much interesting data, I am indebted to Drs. Zoltan Wisinger, J. Murray Aynsley, Robert M. Lloyd-Still, Maurice Despinoy, and Alain Plénel. Data on Virgin Islands patients transferred to St. Elizabeth's Hospital were obtained through the courtesy of Dr. Winfred Overholser.

In the Virgin Islands, I am appreciative of the observations in the areas of family organization and child raising contributed by my wife, Helen Strong Weinstein, from her experience as housewife, member of community groups, and caseworker for the Welfare Department. I am grateful in many ways for the help given by my colleague in the Bureau of Mental Health, Miss Joy Schulterbrandt, now of McGill University, and to Miss Louise James of the

Bureau of Public Health Nursing. Mr. J. Antonio Jarvis, principal of the Lincoln Elementary School, historian, artist, and folklorist, was most generous with time and data. Mr. Jarvis' books, *The Virgin Islands and Their People* and *A Brief History of the Virgin Islands,* made fascinating and valuable references. Miss Bertha Boschulte kindly provided statistical data. I had a number of informative discussions with Mrs. Paula Renner, principal of the Anglican School in St. Thomas, and Mrs. Anita Reynolds of Christiansted, St. Croix, formerly psychologist for the Virgin Islands Department of Health. For information about the Puerto Rican community, I am particularly indebted to Mrs. Lorraine Sevilla and Dr. André Joseph. I would like to thank Mrs. Violet Waddell for her help in the preparation of the manuscript.

EDWIN A. WEINSTEIN, M.D.

CONTENTS

15

CULTURAL ASPECTS
OF DELUSION

INTRODUCTION

IN THIS MONOGRAPH the delusions of psychotic patients will be considered as modes of adaptation to stress. While such delusions are generally classed as forms of deviant behavior apart from cultural goals and social institutions, the behavior still operates in the framework of a culture (Cameron, 1959). It has been shown that many cultures provide specific channels for the reduction of tension (Hallowell, 1938, 1940; Honigmann; Stainbrook); and anthropologists generally have studied delusions in the same context as myths, dreams, magic, religion, witchcraft, and kinship systems. Psychiatrists, on the other hand, have approached the subject of delusions and hallucinations largely in terms of individual motives and conflicts and from the standpoint of disturbances of brain function. There has been relatively little interest in delusions as cultural phenomena. The emphasis has

21

not been on delusional content, but on what have been thought to be the underlying basic psychological and physiological mechanisms.

Psychoanalysts have regarded delusions either as wish-fulfilling fantasies or as denials and projections of some unacceptable wish or drive, usually one dealing with sex or aggression. While the stress-relieving aspects of delusional systems have been recognized, such adaptive functions have been thought to be in the discharge of erotic and destructive impulses and the gratification of unsatisfied infantile wishes. The clinical observation that patients persistently cling to false beliefs despite all contrary evidence seems to give support to the idea that the delusions are powered by, and are manifestations of, biological and instinctive drives.

The "organic" views of delusions and confabulations[1] combine the ideas of "dreams of glory" and defects in perception, cognition, and memory. The explanation of confabulation most frequently given in textbooks of psychiatry is that it is a compensation for loss of memory. The fact that many patients with delusions and confabulations of even quite terrifying content appear serene and unworried has been variously attributed to "lack of affect," "loss of insight," and "loss of motivation."

While "organic" and "dynamic" interpretations of delusions differ in many respects, they show certain common features in respect to the relationships of language and

1. A confabulation is defined as a false narration of an event or series of events. It is differentiated from a delusion in that it is more apt to tell a story and specifically name persons, places, incidents, and periods of time, while a delusion in this sense is timeless and limitless. In this monograph no differentiation is made as to their significance.

reality. In each, a delusion is defined as a distortion of reality, and the symbolic unit is equated with some physiologically or psychologically defined entity, such as an emotion, drive, or neural deficit. Thus, sexual delusions have been interpreted as the result of an impairment of ethical sense, a loss of inhibition, and the release of hitherto repressed impulses. Psychoanalytic explanations often postulate a one-to-one relationship between symbol and referent, such as Freud's statement that a hat stands for the male genital organs. The appearance of a threatening person in a delusion similarly is taken to be the representation of the deluded one's father. Actually, according to psychoanalytic theory, the presenting symbol is relatively unimportant and a repressed homosexual impulse, for example, may be represented in many ways. Cultural factors are not regarded as important in determining the specific content of delusions, but rather are regarded as significant in modifying the basic drives, such as the Oedipus complex, that are thought to underlie delusional systems.

In this monograph, a cultural-linguistic orientation to delusions will be taken. Delusions are considered as symbolic or socially organized units rather than psychological or physiological entities. As a social process, a delusion is not an analogue of a drive or a motive. It is a mode of adaptation to stress, and like comparable symbolic patterns such as humor, proverbs, clichés, slogans, prayer, profanity, vows, and dreams, a delusion derives its function and meaning in a particular spatiotemporal and cultural context. A delusion cannot be defined as a distortion of reality because all cultures and all languages "distort" the physical world to some degree. Nor is a delusion designed to conceal or disguise instinctive drives, but it is a form of metaphor or allegory in which the patient portrays his problems and experiences. By reason of the patient's participation in his culture and through the patterns of social relatedness subserved by the symbols, they are *felt* as particularly meaningful and valid. While delusions are ways of expressing motives and feelings, the nature of such motives and feelings are in considerable part determined by the role of the symbolic element in a cultural pattern.

The ideas of language upon which these concepts are based come largely from the writings of Karl Lashley, Edward Sapir, and the body of theory known as the Sapir-Whorf hypothesis. An outline of some of the fundamental points will be given. Language is the product of an interaction in the environment and its use depends on the capacity of the nervous system to perceive selectively and generalize from among the details of stimuli. One is unaware of the interactive processes of symbol formation, and what we hear, see, and feel is regarded as intrinsic to the stimulus without knowledge of the organizing activity. Lashley states that "thoughts come in syntactical form without effort and without knowledge of how that form is achieved."

Symbols do not stand for things but for *relationships* and *categories*. They take on form and meaning not through the intrinsic properties of their stimuli or the physiological components of the symbolic act but by reason of the place of the element in a pattern. Whorf comments that the concept "blue" could have no meaning in a world where everything was blue. We hear the melody rather than the individual notes, and a tune played in a different key sounds the same provided the notes bear the same temporal and spatial relationship to one another. A movement cannot be defined in terms of its neuromuscular components but only as it fits into some program of action. Meaning is determined not only in a spatiotemporal pattern but in a socially determined organization or category. What we call a chair not only depends on a certain spatial relationship among several selected component parts but on a socially fixed classification. Thus when a "chair" is up against a bar in a cocktail lounge, it is a "stool." The same physical stimulus that is felt as painful when it is administered by the hypodermic needle of a medical missionary may be perceived as ecstasy in the course of a ritual ceremony.

Linguists of the Sapir-Whorf persuasion consider language to be a system of arbitrarily chosen symbols. That is, the designation "chair" does not come from any of the physical properties of the object or from the physiology of sitting down. Yet, for the speakers of any language, symbols are not arbitrary but "natural." A word like "fracture" sounds like something breaking, and a word like "juicy" practically exudes juiciness. A rose by any other name would probably not smell as sweet. While the problem of sound-meaning correlation is still a subject of investigation, it is true that speakers of another language get the same feeling from other designations. The feeling that things *are* what they are and are what they are called is derived from social transactions in a particular cultural group, as well as being determined by the way elements fall into spatiotemporally organized patterns. Thus, children learn to talk through an interaction in their environment of which they are quite unaware. A child uses intricate grammatical constructions and puts words in their proper context without any conception of the rules of syntax. An infant forms more or less unintelligible sounds like "ga" and "da." The adult responds to only some of these, and they come to have meaning for the child in the context of the interpersonal situation. When a parent attends selectively to the "ga" and reinforces certain facial grimaces rather than the glubs, snorts, sniffs, clicks, and other facial-lingual-respiratory synkinesias, then we may suppose that "ga" is on its way to becoming a word, and the facial movement a smile. Yet "ga" does not stand for a thing or an act but for a situation. Similarly, when a child says he is "tired," this is not simply the verbal expression of a physiologically measurable state. It is the product of an interaction that includes his experience in situations where Mother has said she is tired and his anticipation of the events that may follow such a statement. Further, the very language that is used is an important factor in the determination of the feeling of being tired. In Sapir's words:

Even comparatively simple acts of perception are very much more at the mercy of social patterns called words than we might suppose. If one draws some dozen lines, for instance, of different shapes, one perceives them as divisible into such categories as "straight," "crooked," "curved," "zigzag" because of the classificatory suggestiveness of the linguistic terms themselves.

The Sapir-Whorf hypothesis states that language heuristically shapes our experiencing of the physical world. Whorf introduces his classical paper on *The Relation of Habitual Thought and Behavior to Language* with the following quotations from Sapir:

Human beings do not live in the objective world alone, nor alone in the world of social activity as ordinarily understood, but are very much at the mercy of the particular language which has become the medium of expression for their society. It is quite an illusion to imagine that one adjusts to reality essentially without the use of language and that language is merely an incidental means of solving specific problems of communication or reflection. The fact of the matter is that the "real world" is to a large extent unconsciously built up on the language habits of the group. . . . We see and hear and otherwise experience very largely as we do because the language habits of our community predispose certain choices of interpretation. (P. 134)

These ideas were presented in a comparison of North American Indian languages with what Whorf called Standard Average European (SAE) languages. It was shown that Indians formed concepts and communicated in a quite different grammatical structure. Yet they, like the speakers of any language, felt that they were reporting the events of the world in the only way in which they could be accurately represented. For example, in English we designate past, present, and future by the use of three tenses of verbs.[2] Some Indian languages, however, do not have such built in verb forms to indicate past, present, and future. Instead, the verb suffix may give the relationship of the speaker to the event. Thus, if it has rained, the verb form tells whether the speaker has seen it with his own eyes, or whether he has seen evidence such as a footprint, or whether it is something that he has been told. The date of the event may be conveyed implicitly in the situation or may be indicated by a qualifying statement. In English, "fist" is a noun, while in Hopi it is a

2. Dr. George Trager in a personal communication states that English has only two tenses, present and past, but many "modes" as present future *will go,* past future *would go,* present potential *can go,* past potential *could go,* etc.

verb. Whorf believed that European languages imaginatively concretize time and events in spatial metaphors so that temporal units in their linguistic form are placed in the same category as "things." Whorf notes that the Hopi do not use spatial metaphors unless physical space is actually involved. Thus they do not "grasp the thread" or "lose touch." He suggests these background phenomena of language have profoundly influenced the space-time-matter classification of our universe. We use certain grammatical forms not because they are actually necessary for the designation of reality but because we *feel* that they are. Sapir comments that we could say "two house" as well as "two houses" and probably no English-speaking high school French student can understand why he must learn to classify the environment in terms of gender. Yet such redundancies of language operating outside awareness serve to shape our view of reality.

Members of different cultures differ in the way they determine the relevance of the physical components of the referent to the name or symbolic unit. They differ in what are felt to be similarities and dissimilarities. For the Eskimos, many generic entities are subsumed under what we call snow. They have individual names for such different varieties of snow as dry, powdery, soft, wet, and so forth. While we recognize such qualities, they are still all called "snow." Similarly, Dorothy Lee, writing of the Trobriand Islanders, states that they divide a kind of yam into different entities depending on the state of ripeness and the use to which it is put, as in a marriage ceremony, gift, and so forth. Strauss quotes the anthropologist Robert Pehrson as saying that Laplanders have the same word for "people" and "reindeer." This does not mean that the Laplander cannot distinguish a man from a reindeer, or that the Eskimo does not know the relationship of dry snow and wet snow any more than the speaker of English does not know that he does not actually "grasp" the thread. Rather it is a feeling of what something *ought* to be called and what is the *right* name much as one would judge a correct style. Things are felt as like or unlike in terms of the way they form social and subsistence categories. In this sense "people" and "reindeer" are components of a single whole.

The argot of special groups provides numerous examples of the way language structures the feeling of reality. Lay speakers refer to "ship" and "boat" more or less interchangeably, but for naval personnel to confuse the terms would be unthinkable. Similarly, in an installation a thousand miles from the sea one speaks of "going ashore," "visiting the head," and going from one "deck" to another. The speaker "knows" he is not on a ship, but the sense of meaning and the quality of feeling depend on the use of such language against the implicit background of more referential forms of speech.[3] Similarly, the relationship to more conventional language is one factor in the particular feelings associated with the use of poetry, humor, slogans, slang, and proverbs.

Language not only classifies the physical world but it defines identity for its speakers. The term "identity" will be used to denote the cultural orientation and social categorization through which we order our environment. The expression "sense of identity" refers to the *feeling*

3. Referential symbols are universally accepted ones such as letters, numbers, and systems of scientific nomenclature used primarily for purposes of reference and communication. They are contrasted with condensed or experiential symbols that express feelings and derive their meaning to a greater extent in the social context.

that things and events are what they are called. Not only things and events but feelings and motives may be structured in a framework of identity as the writings of Mills, Lindesmith and Strauss, and Foote have suggested. Thus motives are defined as, "rationalizations of acts whereby one relates his acts to previous experience and to the values of the groups to which he must justify his behavior (Lindesmith and Strauss, 1949)."

Foote expands this definition to include the place of the motive as a response to stress in a program of action:

Motivation refers to the degree to which a human being as a participant in the on-going social process defines a problematic situation as calling for a particular act . . . with more or less anticipated consummations and consequences—whereby the organism releases the energy appropriate to performing it.

Symbols should be thought of as transcending motives and feelings as the latter are conventionally designated. For example, while a prayer may be regarded as on the one hand a communication with the Deity or on the other as the verbal expression of religious ardor, love, fear, or awe, the meaning and quality of the feeling derive in large part from the worshiper's relationship in his group. A vivid picture of the way motives and reality are perceived in the context of identity is given by the historian Huyzinga in his account of a medieval nun toiling under her bundle of faggots and feeling her experience to be that of Christ bearing His Cross. Similarly, the validity, purpose, and passion felt by a knight making a vow to fast depended on the significant role of the ritual of food privation in chivalric society. As Huyzinga suggests, such a vow seemed to fulfill many needs: moral,

religious, romantic, ascetic, and erotic. Yet such fulfillment would occur only in a culture in which fasts and
feasting were a central symbolic theme and source of
identity.

In situations of stress, language is more readily equated
with reality by its speakers, although in fact it is less
referential. The capacity for complex interaction in the
environment is impaired, and the events of the physical
world classified in more comprehensive black and white
fashion. The number of channels of relatedness is reduced,
and the speaker becomes even less aware of the interactive
processes of language, regarding the product of the interaction as the very essence of reality. Language becomes
highly stereotyped, and a single symbolic unit such as
a cliché, delusion, confabulation, or other metaphor
serves as a condensed representation of problems and
relationships. Such forms of language are not only indicators of stress but measures of the adaptation.

Observations of the behavior of patients following head
injury (Weinstein and Kahn, 1955; Weinstein, Kahn, and
Malitz, 1956; Weinstein, 1958) pointed out that such
phenomena as confabulations, delusions, and disorientation were forms of language serving as modes of adaptation to stress. It was shown that while a confabulation
ostensibly referred to events of the past, it symbolized
some current problem, usually one dealing with some
aspect of the patient's incapacity. Thus, a patient with
a disability in writing and speaking might offer a confabulation about having written a speech. Or someone
with an intellectual deficiency might tell a story of having
engaged in "counterintelligence activities." The particular
language in which the confabulation (or delusion) was
couched often indicated the values of the patient's family

background or culture, that is, the preferred channels of relatedness in his group. Thus paratroopers who sustained a head injury in an automobile accident confabulated that they had been in plane crashes, or had fallen out of an airplane, or told how a hole had been knocked in the top of the parachute. A patient who had sustained a head wound in the Korean War and who attributed his prolonged hospitalization to his wife's neglect told a long story about the film *Samson and Delilah*. Whether such stories and beliefs are true or not, the patient metaphorically depicts his disability and achieves a sense of identity. While he may deny the physical reality, he attains a "social reality."

While phenomena such as confabulation and disorientation for place are often attributed in the literature to loss of memory or defects in perception, it could be shown that the confabulatory or disoriented patient was aware in other contexts of what had happened to him and where he was. Thus a patient might deny having had an operation on his head but complain about the "sawing and the hammering" done by the doctors. Or he might call the hospital by another name but give an accurate designation when telling of how his brother had been a patient. Such observations indicate how confabulations and delusions derive so much of their meaning against the background of the knowledge of the physical reality.

In these previous studies, the content of delusions and confabulations was correlated with each patient's family background. Thus, when a patient conceptualized his interpersonal relationships by saying that someone was poisoning his food, he usually came from a family where the preparing, dispensing, and consumption of food were important vehicles for relatedness and communication. In the present study, the delusions and other symbolic patterns occurring in patients of the several cultural groups in the Virgin Islands will be compared. For a total of 148 subjects seen in the Knud-Hansen Memorial Hospital of St. Thomas and the Charles Harwood Memorial Hospital of St. Croix the following categories of delusional systems were made:

Children, including delusions about pregnancy
Religion
Witchcraft (obeah)
Death
Physical violence
Sex
Color and race
Food
Money and property
Institutions and ideologies (such as the Church,
    Government, famous people)
Somatic delusions

No differentiation was made among delusions, confabulations, illusions, and hallucinations, the evidence being the patient's verbal report. Records were also made of the expressed fears, worries, preoccupations, rationalizations, and explanations of the illness; excuses to leave the hospital; and formulations of plans for the future. Diagnostic categories were discarded mainly because many of the psychotic episodes were brief and difficult to classify. According to the usually accepted nosology, they included schizophrenic and manic reactions, paranoid states and psychoses associated with alcoholism, epileptic states, and a few senile and cerebrovascular conditions.

It is hoped that the study will be useful in several ways. First, it provides documentation for a particular point of view and furnishes a framework in which relationships of the forms of mental illness to cultural patterns may be studied. Second, it presents ideas about the nature of symbolic functions and delusional systems that may be valuable in the treatment of individual patients. Finally, it offers data that may be used for further studies by social scientists in the West Indies.

1   HISTORY AND PEOPLE

History

THE VIRGIN ISLANDS, purchased from Denmark in 1917, is the most southeasterly situated possession of the United States. The three small, subtropical Caribbean islands of St. Thomas, St. Croix, and St. John, with an area of slightly less than 140 square miles, lie 50 miles east of Puerto Rico. With the adjoining British Virgin group, they form the western boundary of the Lesser Antilles chain. St. Croix, the largest island, with a population of 15,000, is comparatively flat and fertile, while St. Thomas and St. John are mountainous, and the lack of rainfall makes them unsuited for agriculture. St. Thomas is the most populous, and the great majority of its 16,000 inhabitants live in the capital city of Charlotte Amalie, named for a Danish princess. St. John is the smallest, with fewer than 1,000 persons, and most of its 20 square miles

35

are now within the limits of a National Park. The preliminary report of the 1960 census lists a total population of 31,905 for the Territory.

The Danes took formal possession of St. Thomas in 1671, and except for periods of occupation by the British during the Napoleonic Wars, the Danish West India Company and Crown ruled until the transfer to the United States in 1917. St. Croix was purchased by Denmark from France in 1733 after attempts at colonization by the Dutch, English, French, Spanish, and the Knights of Malta. Slavery was introduced into St. Thomas in 1673 after an unsuccessful experience with indentured labor and an economy of tobacco, indigo, cotton, and sugar was established. St. John was settled from St. Thomas, the first plantation being set up in 1717. In 1733 there was an insurrection in St. John, in which the slaves massacred many of the white settlers and ruled the island for six months. The rebellion was put down with the aid of an expedition from Martinique, but St. John remained sparsely inhabited until its recent development as a tourist resort. St. Croix went on to become a typical West Indian sugar island, while St. Thomas, with its strategic position along shipping lanes and the excellent harbor of Charlotte Amalie, developed into a commercial center.

While the history of slavery in the West Indies has been well documented, several features may be cited as relevant to our thesis. On the whole, the conditions of slavery were harsher in the Caribbean than in the American South. There was more absentee ownership in the West Indies, and estate proprietors and managers looked for quick profits and an early return to the mother country. In general, the Europeans who came out to the West Indies were more volatile and shiftless than those who migrated to the mainland colonies, and the violence of life was enhanced by the recurring wars and endemic piracy. The smaller proportion of whites to Negroes made the danger of slave insurrections greater and the punishment for revolts and disobedience more drastic. Slaves multiplied much less rapidly in the West Indies, necessitating greater dependence on the slave trade and the new arrivals from Africa were apt to be less tractable than Negroes born to slavery. Because of the fear of rebellion, community life was greatly limited. Social and religious gatherings were discouraged and singing, dancing, and drum beating strictly forbidden.

Probably the most significant aspect of slavery in the light of present-day social institutions was that the tribal and family organization that had existed in Africa was completely broken up. To use a modern term, the slaves were effectively brainwashed in that they were stripped of their identity, even of their names, and forced to take on the value system of their captors. But in considering the legacy of slavery and the plantation system, one must take into account not only the slaves but the masters as well. The loose family arrangements, the virtual polygamy and polygyny, and promiscuous sexual relationships existing in some West Indian groups today have been interpreted both as a persistence of African customs and as a residue of slave attitudes. Yet West Indian planters customarily maintained numbers of Negro and colored mistresses. Writing in about 1800, Bryan Edwards, a Jamaican M.P., estimated that 10,000 West Indian slaves of the driver-artisan class had several "wives." The planters encouraged sexual promiscuity in the mistaken belief that frequent changes in partners increased fertility. The love of ostentation and the improvidence attributed to slaves can hardly have been less than that of a rich West Indian planter. The contempt for field work and the harsh treatment given to slaves by black overseers seem in full emulation of many owners. These points are brought up to indicate that an understanding of the origin of West Indian social patterns must include an awareness of eighteenth- and nineteenth-century European life.

St. Thomas became prosperous in the early and late years of the eighteenth century and the first half of the nineteenth century. It was a provisioning and transshipment point for ships plying to and from Europe, North America, the West Indies, and South America. The natural advantages of location and a good harbor were enhanced by the neutrality of Denmark in the frequent wars of the European powers and during the American Revolution. (In contrast, the Dutch island of St. Eustatius, another "scrub-covered rock," changed hands ten times in the wars between 1664 and 1674.) In wartime, the Danes were able to trade with belligerent nations. In times of nominal peace, ships from St. Thomas were engaged in the illegal evasions of the trade regulations set up by the mercantilistic systems of England, France, and Spain. Colonies were obliged to send their produce to the mother country and receive the manufactures of only that country in return. When it was more profitable to trade elsewhere, the ports of Charlotte Amalie and Christiansted in St. Croix furnished convenient entrepôts. For example, a ship obliged to carry only British materials might take on its cargo in St. Thomas, then stop briefly in British Tortola for a token loading and papers, and proceed to England with the sugar, molasses, and indigo, which originally came from the French islands. American colonists evading the Navigation Acts used the Danish islands. After 1767 the Danish government permitted St. Thomas to trade with any European country or colony. It was not difficult to gain Danish nationality, and British and French subjects, forbidden to trade with other countries, could become Danes practically overnight. Caribbean governors and officials of the eighteenth century were often connivers at and even participants in illegal trade, and St. Thomas became known as a nest of international smugglers. It was to close this loophole that the British occupied the Danish islands in the Napoleonic Wars.

St. Thomas had a highly cosmopolitan society and, in comparison with other Caribbean islands, a great degree of economic mobility. In the eighteenth century, the Europeans on the island were mainly Dutch, but in the nineteenth century other nationalities predominated. A census of 1837 lists 450 Creoles (native-born whites), 400 Jews, 250 Danes and Germans, 250 British and Americans, and 132 others. The Jews, who were of Sephardic origin, came after the destruction of the commerce of the Dutch island of St. Eustatius during the American Revolution.

St. Thomas has long been a haven for exiles. French Protestants came there after the revocation of the Edict of Nantes in 1685, and refugees fled there after the Santo Domingo slave insurrection of the 1790's and the Latin American revolutions of the nineteenth century. Probably the best known of the refugees was Santa Anna, the Mexican dictator and conqueror of the Alamo. The population of St. Thomas rose from 4,371 in 1773 to 14,022 in 1835, with a more than fifteenfold increase in the number of free colored inhabitants. In the 1840's only 2,500 of the 14,000 people of St. Thomas gained their living from plantations, and at the time of the emancipation in 1848, half of the colored and Negro residents were already free. They earned their living as craftsmen, warehouse-men, and house servants, while women were employed as seamstresses, cooks, laundresses, and market vendors. The economy of St. Croix was based on sugar, though the fertility of the island permitted the raising of other crops. In 1798 there were 22,250 slaves, and this figure did not change appreciably until emancipation. The majority of the St. Croix planters were British, having come after the growth of the large sugar estates had forced them out of the Leeward Islands.[1]

In the latter half of the eighteenth century, the Danish attitude toward slavery became progressively more liberal. The policy of the government was facilitated by the fact that the planter class did not have influence in Copen-hagen comparable to that of the British West India lobby in London. Beginning with the Royal Ordinance of 1755, religious education and Christian burial were provided and a slave could not be sold without his consent unless the whole estate changed hands. A slave was allowed to keep money earned during his spare time, and he could buy his freedom at a price fixed by the Government. (With the expectation of abolition the prices of slaves came down to about one-fourth of what they were in the United States.) Children of white fathers were declared free; and Denmark, in 1803, was the first country to abolish the slave trade. (Britain did so in 1807, while the United States did not stop it effectively until the Civil War.) Larsen, a Lutheran minister in St. Thomas, stated that there was probably no other place where as high a

1. The family of the mother of Alexander Hamilton came to St. Croix from Nevis not long after the purchase of the island by the Danes.

proportion of slaves could read as in the Danish West Indies.

The events following the Proclamation of Emancipation of 1848 are of especial interest in that they illustrate different forms of identity and reactions to its loss in the plantation society of St. Croix as compared with the largely commercial establishment of St. Thomas. It was announced by Governor Peter Von Scholten that slaves would be free after a waiting, or apprentice, period of twelve years, while children born during this time would be free. The plan was greeted with satisfaction in St. Thomas, but in St. Croix there was rioting in Fredriksted, though without bloodshed. To forestall more violence, Governor Von Scholten acceded to the demands of the slaves for immediate freedom. Despite the fact that he was known as their benefactor, the slaves did not make the proclamation a cause for rejoicing but instead marched on Christiansted the following day. This time Danish troops fired, killing several people and precipitating more violence. Von Scholten was severely criticized and removed from office for not having put down the insurrection with a firm hand. It is ironical that the slaves should have rebelled against one of the great humanitarians of the era.

The riots are generally attributed to disappointment with the announcement that freedom was not to be granted for twelve years. Yet there was more violence after the concession was made than there had been before. Why? It is likely that for the Crucian slave the prospect of freedom was frightening, since it meant the loss of the identity that derived from the master-slave relationship. In addition, the provision that children born during the waiting period would be free may have caused anxiety as it meant that slaves would lose even the respect of their children. One of the signs carried by the rioters read, "Our children free and we slaves." In St. Thomas, on the other hand, a considerable degree of identity and status had already been achieved in terms of occupation.

Beginning in the 1840's the prosperity of the islands steadily declined. The sugar of St. Croix could not meet the competition of large-scale production in Cuba and in Asia, and the development of the beet sugar industry in Europe. With steam transportation and improved modes of communications at sea, the strategic location of St. Thomas was minimized. There was a temporary revival of trade during the American Civil War when blockade runners, privateers, and the United States Navy all used the port of Charlotte Amalie. The population shrank from a peak of 43,178 to 26,051 at the time of the transfer to United States sovereignty in 1917. While St. Croix remained rural after emancipation, it did not develop the small peasant holdings that succeeded the plantation system in some of the British islands. A labor act provided for the maintenance of laborers on the estates by yearly contract with stipulated hours and wages up to fifteen cents a day. There was serious discontent in St. Croix and there were a number of riots, including a quite bloody uprising in 1878. Because of the economic drain and the depressed condition of the mother country after the disastrous war with Prussia and Austria, Denmark sought to sell her West Indian islands to the United States as early as 1865. An agreement for the sale of St. Thomas and St. John was actually made between the Danes and Secretary Seward but was not ratified by Congress. The final purchase of the three islands for twenty-five million dollars in 1917 was prompted by the possibility of German seizure during World War I, and the danger to the Panama Canal.

The Danes were administrators and soldiers with a scattering of professional men, but they never settled in large numbers. At the time of the transfer, they composed only about 30 per cent of a white population of fewer than 2,000. Danish rule was authoritarian and the governor, appointed by the king, was usually a military man. Denmark itself was an absolute monarchy from 1660 to 1848. Unlike the situation in the larger British islands, there was no locally elected legislature with power to vote money. It was not until 1865 that the first limited franchise allowed a few members of the propertied class to elect a council. While Danish was the official language, the slaves and freedmen spoke mainly Dutch Creole in the eighteenth century and English thereafter. The Danes favored a highly stratified society based on caste and color. As elsewhere in the West Indies, there was the white European upper class at the top, then the free colored, and then the black freedmen and slaves. The Danes regulated the social and economic activities of even the free colored class. In 1786, for instance, it was ruled that they could not wear precious stones or give rings as presents in funerals. In 1830 three classes of free colored were decreed, with only the highest permitted to engage in trade. The others were given certificates of respectability signed by the governor, but these and their privileges could be revoked for bad conduct. An ordinance of 1839 provided for free and compulsory education and that lighter-skinned natives might be sent to Denmark for higher education. Such policies denote a different attitude toward Negroes in the Danish West Indian islands than that prevailing in the Southern United States. The Danes aimed to make colored persons as "white" as possible, while in the South the objective was rather to keep them as "black" as possible.

The church has long been an important institution in Virgin Islands history. Like the state, it was authoritarian and paternalistic. The Danish Lutheran Church was the established state denomination.[2] From 1771 there was a prescribed service for Negroes in English and a separate one in Danish. The Moravians, an evangelical missionary sect, were particularly active in the conversion, education, and institution of Christian monogamy among the slaves. The Moravians had somewhat the role of the nonconformist Methodists and Quakers in the British islands, except that their efforts were encouraged by the government and slaveholder opposition was less effective.[3] In contrast to the history of slavery in the United States, the major efforts toward the amelioration of the conditions of slavery were made by organized churches. The many legal holidays in the islands today, such as Holy Thursday and Supplication Day (at the beginning of the hurricane season) are largely of religious origin. The present population is about two-thirds Protestant and one-third Roman Catholic. The Anglicans, who began missionary work at the end of the nineteenth century, are the largest Protestant denomination. The Anglican church in St. Croix dates from 1760, and the first permanent rector came to

2. Recently, the American government found to its embarrassment that as the heir to the Danes it owned the Lutheran Church in Christiansted.

3. Bryan Edwards estimates that in 1787 there were 10,000 converted slaves under the care of the brethren.

St. Thomas in 1824. Church membership has always been an important indicator of respectability, and the churches still play a large formal role in society. Over three-quarters of the marriages are religious ceremonies (Table I), and all public meetings are opened by prayer.

When the islands were acquired by the United States, they were in a severe economic depression, and its effects were accentuated by Prohibition. In the 1930's, 70 per cent of the population was unemployed or underemployed, and 45 per cent lived in one-room shacks. As an American territory, the islands were administered by the Navy until 1931 and then placed under the Department of the Interior. Naval rule was paternalistic with emphasis on health services. An organic act providing for a popularly elected legislature subject to the veto power of the governor was passed by Congress in 1936. The governor is appointed by the President, and his actions are to a degree subject to the direction of the Secretary of the Interior. A special feature of government is that in the continental United States a community of 32,000 persons would be part of a larger urban or county unit. The insular situation necessitates a large number of administrative positions that ordinarily would be filled in smaller numbers at higher echelons. The profusion of government employees is increased by the fact that there are practically no private health or welfare agencies. Following the change from naval to civil administration, the federal government initiated a policy of direct aid and tax benefits that, with the status of a free port and the growth of tourism, has greatly benefited the economy.

Cultural Groups

The 32,000 people of the Virgin Islands fall into a number of fairly well-defined cultural groups. The majority are of mixed African and European ancestry. Those born in the Virgin Islands or of Virgin Islands parents living in the States refer to themselves as natives.[4] Yet this term does not apply to French, Puerto Ricans, or Continentals born in the islands, even if their parents were also born in St. Thomas or St. Croix.[5] People from Tortola or the British islands become "natives" after one or two generations, depending on the degree of their acceptance in the community. There are a few white natives, mainly living in St. Croix. The matter of distinguishing Virgin Islanders from British islanders is complicated by the fact that almost all Virgin Islands natives have relatives in other Caribbean areas as a result of the many migrations that have occurred. The same surnames are found from St. Thomas to Trinidad. At the turn of the century many Virgin Islanders went to work on the Panama Canal, and during World War I there was a large movement to the then Santo Domingo. Early in this century, there was a considerable immigration to St. Croix from St. Kitts and Barbados, and during the past twenty-five years there has been a heavy influx from neighboring Tortola and other Leeward islands. In 1958, 40 per cent of the mothers of

4. There are approximately 12,000 persons born in the Virgin Islands living on the mainland, chiefly in New York.

5. Continentals from the States may become "natives" by marrying a native. Natives of St. Croix are called Crucians.

children born in the Virgin Islands gave as their place of birth one of the British West Indies. It is estimated (because there is no census breakdown by cultural group) that natives make up 60 per cent of the population of St. Thomas and St. John and 40 per cent of that of St. Croix. In this study, all native Virgin Islanders are considered as belonging to the same cultural group, although subcultural differences are noted between Crucians on the one hand and St. Thomians and people from St. John on the other.

In addition to native Virgin Islanders there is a second cultural group made up of emigrants from the British Virgin Islands, particularly Tortola. Their number is difficult to estimate, as many are in American territory under a quasi-legal status, but there are about 1,600 registered British aliens in St. Thomas. Tortola formally became English territory in 1666 and adopted a slave, cotton, and sugar economy, though the very rocky terrain hindered the development of large estates. The island is poor, and the 7,000 people live on small family-owned plots, raising food for local consumption and some livestock for export. The British Virgin Islands actually form an economic unit with the American islands, using United States currency and providing laborers and domestic servants for St. Thomas. In contrast to the paternalism of the American Government, educational and welfare service in Tortola are very limited. Official American policy furthers immigration by the granting of work and visitors' permits, and the right of American citizenship to children of alien parents born in the Virgin Islands. Tortolans are differentiated from native Virgin Islanders more in terms of social class than of ethnic group, and their social organization and symbolic value systems will be considered with those of lower-class Virgin Islanders.

The third cultural group is composed of immigrants from the tiny French island of St. Barthélemy, or St. Bart's, in the *départmente* of Guadeloupe, situated 100 miles to the east and south of St. Thomas. St. Barthélemy, neglected by France and with no schools or roads, was under Swedish sovereignty from 1784 to 1877, though the people continued to speak French. The people are white, are highly interbred, and are probably the descendants of privateers and buccaneers. Migration to St. Thomas began about 1870. The settlers were poor fishermen and farmers who squatted on unoccupied, rocky, arid land. There are two main settlements of French in St. Thomas, one on the waterfront known as Carénage and the other on the hills along the north coast. The French number about 1,500, making up about 10 per cent of the population of St. Thomas. In religion they are Roman Catholic. Because of their general poverty and particularly their habit of going barefoot, they were generally scorned by the natives and derisively called "chachas." Their position as a poor white minority may be compared to that of the other white enclaves in the Caribbean, the "Red Legs" of Barbados and the "Germans" of Jamaica, but with the prosperity of recent years their economic status has risen. Their long history of geographical and social isolation and inbreeding makes the French the most homogeneous in looks, religion, occupation, and social class of the cultural groups of the Virgin Islands.

A fourth cultural group is formed by Puerto Ricans, the great majority of whom have come to St. Croix from the island of Vieques, lying off the southeast corner of the Puerto Rican mainland. The population of Vieques, or Crab Island, consists of Spanish-speaking peasants and the personnel of an American Naval base located there. Migration to St. Croix began in 1917 when agents of the West Indian Sugar Company recruited laborers for the cane fields. Today, they work as agricultural laborers in St. Croix and on both islands as mechanics, laborers, and shopkeepers. Puerto Ricans from Vieques are almost uniformly the color of *café au lait* and are of mixed white, Negro, and Indian ancestry. They make up about 40 percent of the population of St. Croix and about 15 per cent of that of St. Thomas.

Americans from the United States who have come to the Virgin Islands are known as "Continentals." They have not been included in the formal study, although they appear in Table III for purposes of comparison, because of the difficulty in obtaining material on the cultural background and because their stay in the islands is so often a brief one. Some have come to retire, others to go into business or government, and others have sought relief from the tensions of stateside life. The islands functioned for a time in the thirties as a divorce mill, and a considerable number who came because of marital troubles have remained. They are a shifting group because so many of them return to the States after finding that the difficulties of housing and the expenses of living are too great and that the promise of solving their problems in a tropical paradise is unfulfilled. Continentals own and manage the hotels and the larger businesses. They provide much of the leadership in cultural and educational activities, but generally avoid political activity and are not noted for churchgoing. Only a handful of the original Danes remain, but a large Danish consulate is maintained, and several large business establishments are run by Danes who have come to the islands since the transfer.

Five cultural groups—native Virgin Islanders, British Virgin Islanders, French, Puerto Ricans, and Continentals —live in the Virgin Islands. In the succeeding chapters, we do not discuss the Continentals in detail, but we do study the different cultures and the behavior under stress of the Virgin Islanders, the Puerto Ricans, and the French.

2 INSTITUTIONAL SOURCES OF IDENTITY

IN THIS CHAPTER, the derivation of identity through the institutions of nationality, race, social class, family, church, and occupation among native Virgin Islanders will be considered. The gaining of identity in terms of national and ethnic grouping is a simpler matter for the French and the Puerto Ricans than for Virgin Islanders, if for no other reason than that they are minority groups speaking their particular language. Although native Virgin Islanders are American citizens either by birth or under the terms of the transfer of sovereignty from Denmark, older persons still do not feel wholly American. Many, in fact, refer to Continentals as "Americans." The status of the islands as a distant territory, to a considerable extent controlled and subsidized by Washington, emphasizes their insular character. The fact that Virgin

Islanders do not vote in national elections or have representation in Congress is another aspect of their separation. There does not seem to be the degree of fixation on being American that there is in Barbados on being "British." A few better-class people rather self-consciously stress their Danish origin, but this does not extend beyond trips to Denmark and the cultivation of Danish acquaintances.

There is little sense of being West Indian, and scant interest is shown in the West Indies Federation. Suggestions that the Virgin Islands join with Puerto Rico to form a more viable economic unit are rejected. Contempt for and resentment toward migrants from the British islands are commonly expressed with attention being directed to their poverty, violent behavior, and harsh methods of child raising, and they are referred to as "garrots." Most natives are more apt to consider themselves as Crucians or St. Thomians rather than Virgin Islanders. There is considerable rivalry between the two islands expressed mainly in accusations of political favoritism. In St. Croix there is much jealousy between the towns of Christiansted and Fredriksted. Actually, one hears talk of being a Virgin Islander or a St. Thomian or a Crucian most often when resentment is being expressed or a complaint made about discrimination by some governmental or political agency.

Race and Color

The role of race and color in the establishment of identity differs considerably from the situation in the continental United States. There are not only no legal regulations concerning color, but there are very few exclusive organizations that tacitly bar persons of color. While color gradations are significant components of social status, the Virgin Islander does not identify himself as a Negro to the degree that most colored persons do in the States. There is not an arbitrary division into white and Negro groups in which people of mixed ancestry are classed as Negro. People are described as black, brown, red, and white, dark and light, but the terms "mulatto" and "Negro," with their implications of miscegnation and race, are not often used.[1] Caucasian standards of physical attractiveness prevail, and light skin, straight or wavy hair, and European features are valued as attributes of beauty. Light-skinned children are preferred, as it is felt that such physical qualities will enhance chances for success in life.

Historically, skin color has been an important determinant of social position, and wealthier families tend to be lighter skinned. Under the Danes, prestige was based on wealth and skin color, and at the time of the transfer the upper class, who numbered perhaps 10 per cent, included not only Europeans but light natives, Haitians, and other West Indians. The importance of color is diminishing, however, particularly in St. Thomas, and in the past twenty-five years more and more darkly pigmented people have achieved status by reason of education and ability. Another factor in the lack of any rigid demarcation by color is that members of the same family may differ a good deal in their shading. In a community as small as

1. Jarvis states that the term "negar" may be used to describe conduct as mean, niggardly, and uncouth, but only indirectly to indicate race.

the Virgin Islands everyone's ancestry is known and few persons try to "pass," a practice that, when present, enhances color consciousness.

It is, of course, impossible to separate color from the other components of social status. Much of the prestige of white Continentals derives from their stateside origin, comparative wealth, and often better education and professional training. Despite their white color, the local French were long despised for their poverty. There is little sense of Negro solidarity, and Negroes from the States in their early years may be regarded as Continentals. Outsiders, Negro or white, may be resented equally if they are felt to be acting in a superior or critical manner. In fact, there is often more willingness to accept criticism from white Continentals. The difficulties of a former Negro governor are said to have arisen from his having brought down a number of Negro officials from the States. Natives may express such feeling in the comment, "We were free when your ancestors were picking cotton and walking barefoot," a remark that also indicates local attitudes toward menial labor and the proprieties of dress. The recent appointment of a white native as governor received wide popular approval. Any feeling about color was far transcended by the satisfaction over the honor to a Virgin Islander and the step taken toward self-government.[2]

There is more equation of social status with color in St. Croix than there is in St. Thomas. The historical factors

2. This might be compared with an incident cited by Douglas Manley in which a white candidate for office in the 1958 election in Jamaica issued a letter to the press under the headline, "I cannot help my colour."

of the plantation system in St. Croix have been mentioned, and even today the island has a more limited economy and more of a seigniorial flavor. Continentals who have moved to St. Croix in the past few decades are more apt to live as country squires than to work in the shops as they do in St. Thomas. While very few, if any, of the whites in St. Croix are the descendants of the plantation owners, they approximate the role of the old European upper class. Writing of late nineteenth-century St. Croix, Jarvis speaks bitterly of the "Bourbons" who blocked economic progress and seduced "ripe black girls." Certainly the heritage of the days of slavery and semibondage, when one of the few avenues for economic and social advancement was to have a child by a white father, was more lasting in St. Croix than in St. Thomas.

Many Virgin Islanders feel that what color prejudice exists was brought in by Americans after the transfer. They contrast the decorum of the Danes with the rowdy behavior and taunts about color made by some American sailors and marines during the naval administration. Even today, sailors are ignored socially. Also Virgin Islanders visiting the States or serving there in the Armed Forces during the last war were subjected to discrimination. Some tension results when American visitors lump all natives together as Negroes either in a deprecating fashion or in a well-intentioned gesture toward democracy and tolerance. Amusing and embarrassing incidents have also arisen when race-conscious Negroes from the States have attempted to awaken pride in their black ancestry among Virgin Islanders (some of whom are of perhaps one-eighth African descent plus Danish, French, English, Dutch, and even Chinese ancestry).

Social Class

In contrast to former days, social class among native Virgin Islanders is difficult to define in terms of the usual criteria of family, income, occupation, education, place of residence, and church affiliation. Apart from a few individuals, there is no upper class in the sense that it exists in the continental United States, Europe, and South America. In Virgin Islands society, there is no educated aristocracy of inherited wealth and no group devoted to leisure or philanthropy; these vocations are filled by Continentals. With the rapid economic growth of recent years, many of the more prosperous citizens are of humble origin. There are no society columns in the newspapers, no prominent and exclusive social clubs, and the organizations that enjoy the greatest prestige are the Women's League, a civic group, and the Rotary Club. The educational indexes of class are also different from those in the continental United States. Some prominent persons have not completed a high school education, since a four-year course became available only in the 1930's. The census of 1950 showed that only 333 people had graduated from high school. In contrast to the policy in the British islands, the American government has favored the practice of hiring natives for government positions in preference to Continentals, so that some teachers, for example, are poorly trained and do not automatically fall into what would correspond to the middle class in the mainland United States. While there has long been compulsory education, the practice of "social promotion" in the schools makes it difficult at times to know what grade has been actually mastered. In one instance, a now successful businessman took advantage of the G.I. bill for veterans (and the benefits for his several children) by returning to the third grade!

Some Federal jobs, which in the States would be in a lower-class category, may place a Virgin Islander at a comparatively high income level. The tourist industry makes such ordinarily lower-class jobs as waiter and taxi-driver comparatively lucrative. Similarly, place of residence does not automatically determine social class, since there are few exclusive neighborhoods, and an expensive house may stand next to a shack.

Because of the difficulty of defining criteria for social class objectively, for purposes of this study I have designated two classes, upper and lower, simply on the basis of listing in the telephone directory. The possession of a telephone would place about 25 per cent of the native Virgin Islands population in the upper class. Defined in this way, the upper class includes higher salaried government servants, professional men, skilled artisans, graduate nurses, and some teachers, social workers, salespeople, and shop proprietors. The lower class would be comprised of laborers, other unskilled and semiskilled workers, and domestics. The lower class also includes the very great majority of persons from Tortola, and, as mentioned, no attempt is made to distinguish them from people actually born in the American Virgin Islands.

Religious Affiliation

Although religious beliefs and language provide highly important sources of identity for native Virgin Islanders

(Chapter 6), church affiliation is not an important indicator of social class. The great bulk of the population belongs to the Anglican, Lutheran, Moravian, and Roman Catholic churches; and the few charismatic, or "outside," sects have only a small number of adherents. For most of the main churches the Virgin Islands are still a missionary area and ministers are appointed from the States. An exception is the Methodist Church, which has a minister from the Leeward Islands to serve its predominantly British West Indian congregation. It is also exceptional in that it is the only larger church that does not draw its membership from all social strata. The analysis of the membership of the other large churches contrasts with Frazier's analysis of the social stratification in the States, where upper-class Negroes go to the Episcopal, Presbyterian, and Congregational churches, the middle class to the larger Baptist and Methodist groups, and the lower class joins the small sects. Also in the States the churches provide leadership in the fight for Negro rights and entry into the ministry is a means of attaining prestige. The churches do not have this role in the Virgin Islands.

The Family as an Institution

Family organization as such will be considered in the next chapter, but the family as an institution does not seem to be an important source of identity. As will be described, the household group is often not the economic unit. There is not a great deal of family pride and solidarity, and the achievements of one member do not automatically confer status on another. A person with an important professional job may have a relative working, say, as a porter in New York. Likewise, native Virgin Islanders do not express responsibility to any extent for the derelictions of relatives. Families tend to scatter, and even in the Islands a person may hardly know his grandparents or some of his siblings.

The failure of the family to become an important social institution is closely related to the role of old people. In general, they do not have much authority but do not seem to mind the diminished status that comes with old age. The fact that they rarely control substantial amounts of money or property means that they do not command the allegiance or control the destinies of younger family members. Even the parents of highly successful people may continue to live in quite primitive surroundings. While people may not conspicuously neglect aged relatives, there is no great sense of filial piety as such. The common attitude is that children will be good to parents if parents have been good to them. There is not nearly the idealization of the mother and respect for the father that occurs in Puerto Rican society. The aged seem to stand comparative idleness and boredom well and are useful, particularly in caring for children whose parents go out to work. The role of old persons varies a good deal with social class, as in the lower class a grandmother may be the head of a household composed largely of children.

The following is an account of a visit to a lower-class "grandmother household":

CASE REPORT

Miss M was seen in her home because of her complaint of gas in her head. Previously she had had weakness in her chest, which she had diagnosed through McDonald's *Almanac*. She then caught a cold in her throat when her hat blew off while she was hurrying home from church one night. She then had a dream in which God told her to get a dry goat's hoof, burn it to charcoal, grind it, and mix it with coconut oil and put it on her throat. In three days she was cured.

Miss M was seventy-two years old. She was born in Jost Van Dyke (an island in the British Virgin group between Tortola and St. Thomas). She had lived in Haiti for nine years and since coming to St. Thomas had made her living as a baby sitter. Her home was a one-room house partitioned by a drape. It was barely furnished and a charcoal pot with frying fish was on the floor. During the visit four children were staying with her for day care, including a four-months old baby asleep on some bedding on the floor and a creeper tied to her arm by an old soiled garment. Miss M said that the parents provided food and five dollars a month for day care. Sometimes she kept children during the time that their mothers from Tortola were on a 29-day visitor's permit.

She shared her home with a fourteen-months old little girl, Beulah. The child was the daughter of a teacher who used to leave her for day care. Miss M said that she had gotten so fond of the child and that Beulah cried so much when her mother came for her that the mother allowed her to remain.

Occupation

Occupation and economic achievement may form an important basis of identity, but, as elsewhere, this varies a great deal with educational and professional level. Native Virgin Islanders prefer white-collar jobs and have an aversion to manual labor, particularly agricultural work. The laborers in the cane fields of St. Croix are Puerto Ricans or British West Indians. The reasons given are that field work in the hot sun is a relic of slavery and that the poor, arid soil makes agriculture unprofitable. Yet the French have farmed the steep hillsides of St. Thomas, and their ownership of once worthless land has been an important factor in their currently rising prosperity. The intense desire to own and work land present elsewhere in the Caribbean is not marked among Virgin Islanders. The dislike of farming in St. Thomas is even expressed in a disinclination to have some gardens for fruits and vegetables on an island where food is considerably more expensive than in the States or Puerto Rico, even in families where food costs are the major item in the budget.

Native Virgin Islanders have favored jobs in which the overt prestige value is evident. These include the occupations of government servant, agent for large European and American business firms, and taxi driver. One native carried this predilection to the extreme of affixing the names of thirteen firms, for which he had become agent, to his house. Jarvis has commented on the great eagerness of comparatively uneducated women to become stenographers and clerks. There has been less inclination to work at such well-paying trades as those of plumbers, electricians, and carpenters. Small retail stores are more apt to be run by Continentals and Puerto Ricans than by natives. The occupation of taxi driver has particular standing. It involves the important display of a large American car,[3] sometimes furnished with fancy pillows

3. In St. Thomas natives generally prefer standard American makes, Continentals like Volkswagens or other small foreign cars, and the French use pick-up trucks.

and carpets, and the opportunity to act as a local authority and guide to tourists. In St. Thomas, the Taxicab Drivers Association enjoys considerable prestige. Its members include many veterans of military service, a considerable accomplishment in a community where a high proportion of candidates for military service are rejected on the basis of intellectual performance. Even when working on other jobs, taxi drivers are apt to wear their membership badges.

There is a great deal of pride associated with the attaining of a particular job status, often in some contrast to the satisfaction gained from the performance of the work itself, or even from the amount of money made. In the large number of government positions there is emphasis on maintaining the forms of authority and status and going through proper "channels." People are very conscious of what they feel may be infringements on their status. This attitude even extends to domestic service, where a maid will clean inside the house, but will be affronted if asked to pick up outside. One quite intelligent girl had shown so much aptitude while working as a domestic that her employers had offered to send her through her remaining years in high school at their expense. After considering the offer she refused it, confiding that her ambition was to work in a hotel where she could "associate with a lot of rich people." Leisure and play do not tend to be looked upon as a reward for successful accomplishment of tasks. Recently, the director of a summer school for teachers was taken aback when they wanted to celebrate the completion of the term on the night before the examinations rather than after they were completed. The issue was compromised by having the party two nights before.

The rapid economic development of the islands and

the increasing number of federally subsidized government services often place people in positions for which they are not qualified by reason of vocation and training. This accentuates their need to insist on the overt demonstration of the signs and perquisites of status. Despite the jealousy with which rank is guarded, people often do not keep an exclusive professional identity. The holding of two jobs is not uncommon. A person with an important administrative post may work in his store, or a lawyer may be in some form of retail trade.

If someone is dismissed from a job, there is generally very little discussion of its justification in terms of work performance, but rather it is considered on personal grounds. This was illustrated recently when a government commissioner was summarily discharged. There was little interest in the community as to whether he had done his job efficiently. Rather, most people with whom I spoke felt that it didn't matter as he was well off financially. In a situation when someone is discharged for dishonesty, there is surprising tolerance, and a person so involved may get another government job.

In hospital work I was struck by the degree to which staff members structured their relationship to patients in personal terms rather than in terms of their professional identity. An example of this occurred when after a fracas in the ward, a nurse was aggrieved because she felt that I had shown more sympathy to the patient. She was not concerned that the incident might have reflected on her competence as a nurse. Another aspect of the rapid economic and social changes in the islands that affects the gaining of identity through occupation is that there are now very few traditional jobs that are handed down through families.

Other West Indians tend to look on Virgin Islanders

as extravagant and somewhat improvident. Such opinions run from the statement in Sherlock's *History of the West Indies* that the "Virgin Islanders live on the hard work of British immigrants and the bounty of the American government" to the saying that "Tortolans work and St. Thomians steal." While Virgin Islanders do not have the drive of, say, Barbadians, they cannot be characterized as lazy. Yet work is not esteemed for work's sake, or as a virtue in itself. Several employers stated that Virgin Islanders worked well only if a good personal relationship had been built up. This attitude leads some Virgin Islanders to be rather suspicious of Continentals who volunteer for work in the hospital out of a sense of duty and uneasiness about idleness. Someone who works overtime on a job may be teased, and people are very conscious of the exact amount of time put in.

Recently, it was proposed that a number of the numerous holidays during the school year be eliminated so that teachers might leave early enough in the summer to enroll for advanced training. Though officially initiated, the proposal was indignantly rejected by the teachers, because they were more concerned with having the same holidays as other government workers than with their special status as teachers.

To have come up from poverty is not regarded as particularly ennobling, and Virgin Islanders look down on the hard work of poor Tortolans and Puerto Ricans. One of the most bitterly resented affronts in Virgin Islands history was President Hoover's reference to the islands as a poorhouse about which measures should be taken. The Horatio Alger tradition of bootblack to corporation president may be closer to reality in the Virgin Islands than in the continental United States, but it is not sentimentally cherished.

Psychotic Reactions

In considering the relationship of these sources of identity to forms of adaptation to stress, a number of observations are pertinent in psychoses and other clinical states. The lack of identity through nationality and "national" institutions may be reflected in the fact that Virgin Islanders rarely have had delusions about American institutions or people famous in politics or government. One man who had lived in the States for some time had delusions about the F.B.I. In contrast, among patients seen in the "little England" of Barbados there were many delusions about royalty and nobility. There one woman was a niece of Queen Victoria, and another was the "Queen of Barbados, Grenada and Trinidad." Another Barbadian had been adopted by Sir Edward Cunard. One man revealed that he was a member of King Arthur's Round Table, and another reported his conversations with King George about the conduct of World War II.

In situations of stress, symbolism concerning race and color is infrequent among native Virgin Islanders and considerably more frequent in the French and the Continentals. In the native group, delusions, confabulations, and hallucinations dealing with race, color, and heredity were more common among Crucians (three cases) than St. Thomians (one case), as would be expected from the greater emphasis in St. Croix on color as a component of social role. Thus, one black Crucian had delusions about being born of white parents and was preoccupied with the matter of heredity. Continentals, on the other hand, frequently presented delusions having to do with race and color. A European thought the patients on the psychiatric ward would be segregated and the white ones killed. An American tourist developed a highly agitated state centering about the idea that his wife was sleeping with all of the Negroes in their hotel. Race and color symbols also figured in the obsessional phobic and anxiety states seen in Continentals. Women became afraid of being attacked sexually by Negroes. A Continental government employee, who was leaving the Islands as a result of a marital problem, "confided" that he was leaving because of his fear of an imminent uprising such as was occurring in the Congo.

An interesting relationship between the physical environment and psychotic content was shown in the matter of delusions about land. These did not occur among native Virgin Islanders or in Tortolan patients hospitalized in St. Thomas. But when patients from Tortola were interviewed in the mental hospital in Antigua, which services the Leeward Islands, a large number expressed delusions about their land being stolen. Persons who develop psychoses in Tortola are sent directly to Antigua, while St. Thomas takes only those actually living and working in American territory. As has been mentioned, Tortola is an agricultural community, and it is likely that those persons who remain on the island have more of a sense of identity from the land[4] than those who migrate to urban St. Thomas. It is also of interest that in Tortola a large proportion of cases taken to court concern disputes about land. Delusions about land were also common among patients interviewed in St. Lucia, where there is also peasant proprietorship.

4. As reported by Mr. Norman Fowler, editor of the *Tortola Times*, a favorite expression of disgruntled Tortolans is "I can go back to my guinea corn patch."

The attitudes toward work and accomplishment that have been described may be connected with the types of depression that were seen. Virgin Islanders rarely developed the so-called classical depression in which the patient ruminates about his failures and speaks in self-derogatory fashion of not having done his duty. They did show lethargic, withdrawn states with much symbolism of death (see Chapter 5), but the self-demeaning features were absent. The only patient with a classical depression came from an exceptionally successful upper-class family in which attitudes of responsibility, duty, and hard work were stressed.

Suicide is rare among native Virgin Islanders living in the Islands. Over the past five years the rate has been less than one-fourth that in the continental United States, although there is a higher incidence among the Puerto Ricans. With such a small population these figures may not make for a valid comparison, and other factors are involved, but it is significant that Virgin Islanders do not believe that a person could have such a sense of guilt and failure that he could conceivably, in his right mind, kill himself. An interesting example of the contrast between Virgin Island and Continental attitudes occurred in the case of a Continental who was brought to the hospital after he had slashed both of his wrists in a suicidal gesture. He had done so after hearing voices reproach him for not having lived up to his opportunities in life, for not having paid his debts, and for having visited prostitutes. It is not likely that the "voices" would have spoken thus to a native Virgin Islander.

In summary, Virgin Islanders, unlike the French and Puerto Ricans, do not derive identity to any great extent through social patterns involving race and color, national origin, the family, or the church as institutions. Skin color is descriptive rather than classificatory, and the category of "Negro" does not constitute a social entity in the sense that it does in the continental United States. Although Virgin Islanders are conscious of social position, the layers of social stratification laid down in Danish times have become much more fluid. Most Virgin Islanders do not use profession or occupation in the sense that it predetermines attitudes and motives. This might be contrasted to the attitude of the Puerto Rican, who feels that hard work is an attribute of manhood, or that of a professional person who ties up efficient performance with his integrity as a person.

In psychotic reactions, Virgin Islanders rarely refer to national institutions and do not have many delusions or hallucinations about heredity and color. They are not prone to depressions with feelings of failure and self-derogation, and suicide is uncommon.

3 FAMILY ORGANIZATION AND SEX ROLES

THIS CHAPTER DESCRIBES the various types of family organization in native Virgin Islands society and the social roles of adult members as they are determined by sex and age.

Family Organization

As elsewhere in the Caribbean, there are domestic groupings other than the conventional husband-wife-children nucleus predominant in the continental United States. There are consensual unions in which a couple live together as man and wife. In the 1950 census the proportion of persons legally married to those living in consensual relations was roughly three to one. There are also households organized about women and children, from which men are absent or in which they play a minor part.

The incidence of each type of family grouping is determined largely by social class. While in former years it was common for respected citizens to maintain several households, today upper-class parents are usually married, although either may have illegitimate children. Over half the births in the Virgin Islands (all cultural groups) between 1930 and 1958 occurred out of wedlock (O.W.) with a higher incidence for St. Croix than St. Thomas (Table II). While the illegitimacy rate is decreasing in St. Thomas, it is remaining about the same in St. Croix. There are no figures for Virgin Islands parents born in Tortola, but they may be higher as the illegitimacy rate for Tortola itself is estimated at about 80 or 85 per cent.

The legal status of parents does not necessarily determine the composition of the household. A man living in the home as a husband or a companion may not be the father of any of the children, although he may have children elsewhere. One or both parents may have gone to the States or Puerto Rico leaving children in the care of relatives, godparents, or friends. This pattern is especially common in St. John, where an aunt or grandmother is the head of the household. A married couple may have "outside children"[1] in the home. Some couples marry and have children, but for a time continue to live with their respective families, a state of affairs generally attributed to the housing shortage.

In consensual unions, a man and woman, generally

1. An outside child is the illegitimate child of the parent by a person other than the marital partner.

termed companions, live together as husband and wife. In former years, couples might spend a lifetime together and raise children without legal sanction, but today such relationships are more transitory. There is in the lower class a pattern of serial monogamy in which a woman will live with and bear children "for" several men in succession. It is not unusual to find a household where the children bear three surnames. When the children are acknowledged by the father, as they usually are, they take his name; otherwise they have the mother's name. If the mother is married to another man, the child may take either her maiden name or her husband's name.

The mother of an out-of-wedlock child, if she is young, does not leave her home but continues to live with her family. If her father is not at home, as is frequently the case, or even in some cases when he is, the head of the family is her mother, grandmother, or other female relative. The girl may look after her own child, or she may go out to work in the islands or to the States, leaving the child to be cared for by her mother. Some girls have several children in this arrangement. In some households both the girl and her mother may recently have had children. The ramifications of these relationships are often difficult to follow. When a patient in giving his history stated that he was the father of children each aged one year and seven months, I asked if they were twins. "Oh no," he explained, "one a girl in St. Croix had for me, and the other is with its mother in Antigua."

While marriage is regarded as a sign of respectability and is a source of prestige, there are certain socioeconomic factors and attitudes existing among native Virgin Islanders and Tortolans that are relevant to the continued existence of other patterns of family organization. In native Virgin Islands families almost all women work professionally. Depending on social class, they manage shops, work in stores and offices, and are teachers, nurses, servants, and even laborers. Economic prosperity, the growth of tourism, and the comparatively large number of government positions have created a great demand for labor. Domestic help, drawn largely from the British islands, is cheap and readily available even for low-income families, and the housework and a great share of the care of children is entrusted to maids and grandparents. Under prevailing economic conditions, women make as much money as do men in most of the occupations open to them. In the lower class, the custom of women working is so well established that it is the policy of the Department of Social Welfare to help their clients find jobs rather than to subsidize them to stay home with children. In the upper class, employment of women outside of the home is only a matter of recent years and has been made possible by the great economic expansion.

While women, even in comfortable financial circumstances, usually cite economic necessity or boredom at home as the reasons for working, there are other and complementary factors. The occupation of housewife has a low rating. The Virgin Islands woman does not divorce her essential personality from the drudgery and monotony of housework as do many women in the continental United States. Talcott Parsons has described as a primary aim of the middle-class American woman the preservation of the health, integrity, and prestige of her husband. Virgin Islands women, in the great majority of instances, never quite give up their role of breadwinner in deference to their husbands. They seem much less occupied with their home as a sign of conspicuous wealth and prestige than families in the States. Possibly because of the housing shortage, higher costs, and generally lower income, they spend much less time on projects to improve the home— redecorating, refurnishing, etc.—and there is comparatively little entertaining in the home.

Except for a few persons in very prominent positions, women in general do not acquire their major status through the position of their husbands in the community but rather through their own accomplishments.[2] Also, they do not defer outwardly to men simply by reason of their being males. In unhappy marriages they are much less apt to take on the role of a wronged, suffering martyr than are the Puerto Rican women. On several occasions after hearing women tell of how men had beaten them, I enquired sympathetically as to their reaction, expecting to hear a sorrowful or indignant statement that it was no way to treat a woman or that men had no right to act so. Instead, the matter of fact reply was simply, "I knock him back." Native women are not apt to gain their ends by playing the part of the helpless female or acting in a seductive fashion.[3] A federal District Court judge told me that he could recall no divorce suit brought by a

2. The wife of a Continental professional man had directed the performance of a community group. She listed herself formally on the program as Mrs. John Doe, but the native women in the group insisted that she use her own name of Mary Doe as she and not he had done the work.

3. Two of the most famous riots in Virgin Islands history were led by women. "Queen Mary" led an uprising in St. Croix in 1878 and "Queen Coziah," a bamboula dancer, dared Danish troops at the head of a mob in the Mexican silver crisis in 1892. More recently, a champion for woman suffrage chased a dissenting politician from a public meeting with an umbrella. These incidents appear in the tradition of feminine self-sufficiency.

woman on the grounds of her husband's "outside" children.

Many women in the lower class feel that marriage subordinates them to men. They consider that while a companion has equal rights, men expect more service from a wife. For example, a forty-eight-year-old woman who had had eight children "for" several men explained that she had not married before the age of forty-five because she "didn't want to be ruled by men." The arrival of O.W. children does not necessarily tend toward marriage. Even though the prospective father offers to marry the girl, she may refuse on the grounds that she doesn't like him well enough or that her family is critical of him. Sometimes, after a woman has had children and has gotten an established job, she feels more independent and less in need of a husband or companion. Several women who had children by a number of men told me that this arrangement gave each father less authority in the affairs of the home and made her position in dealing with them stronger.

There is little moral stigma attached to such household arrangements, per se. A woman may have several O.W. children and then settle down to a quite respected existence. This attitude might be compared with that of a recently arrived Continental woman who, speaking of a maid in her hotel, confided, "You know, she has three illegitimate children and she is so honest!"

There are a number of customs and legal procedures that may favor nonmarital relationships. It is traditional for marriages to be very elaborate and costly; this, however, can hardly be a very significant reason, as people frequently spend far more than their earning capacity seems to warrant on medical and dental care, gifts, cars, clothes, and so forth. Although the community generally deplores the custom, there are no laws against fornication and adultery in the Virgin Islands.[4] As mentioned, children born in the islands acquire American nationality, and it would be a hardhearted official indeed who would deprive an American citizen of his mother's loving care. According to law, legitimate and illegitimate children share equally in inheritance, and when there is no property to inherit, it does not make quite as much difference who one's father is. One patient told of having brought the father of her two children into Municipal Court in an effort to gain support for them. As the judge was summarily ordering the father to pay, he paused to ask if the couple were married. When informed that they were, he dismissed the case, stating that it had to be referred to the higher District Court. As the woman had no money for a lawyer, she dropped the matter.

Another feature that militates against marriage is the professed expectation by women of violent or irresponsible behavior in men. While this situation occurs frequently enough, in a household composed only of children and adult females it is easy for such a stereotype to be built up. I recall one unmarried woman who, after having complained of how the father of her child had abused and "practically raped" her, proceeded to become pregnant "for" the man again. Another girl, living with her two children in her parents' home, gave as her reasons for not wanting to marry the father the fact that the man was married, her not believing in divorce, and the fear

4. It is of course highly questionable that any such law would reduce illegitimacy. However, laws have a way of expressing how one ought to behave. As things stand, the term "illegitimacy" is a misnomer, as no law is being violated.

that he might be mean to their children. Men and women seem to use the same kind of violence, mainly vocal. I recall a story told by an Antiguan lady about an altercation with a man in a bar in which she invited him to "step outside and settle it right then and there."

Social Roles

Men gain more fulfillment in the role of parent than in that of husband. It should be noted that many of the more enterprising men find opportunity in the islands limited and move to the States. Those who do may return with Continental wives and have their households function on the American middle-class model, with the man as nominal head. With some older couples the family resembles the Victorian type, but the pattern of male domination does not seem to be present even in the upper class to any great extent. In the lower class, particularly, fatherhood confers self-esteem, and it is not uncommon for men to boast openly about the number of children they have, legitimate and illegitimate. In making small talk men will frequently talk of the number of children they have, one remarking that he had a birthday for each month of the year, meaning that he had had a child born in each month. Men jokingly advise one another to have a child in a situation where in the States sexual intercourse would be suggested as a tonic or remedy. While in the States the measure of sexual potency is the number of conquests or the frequency with which the act of intercourse is performed, in the Virgin Islands virility is equated with impregnation, a feature that Jarvis has called "the fertility cult of the Virgin Islands." Some men (and women) claim that they can tell from their feeling during sexual intercourse whether impregnation is occurring. Probably this is one reason why disputes about paternity rarely ensue.

A man is often more willing to accept the financial responsibilities of fatherhood than of marriage. Becoming a father sometimes gives him enough security to enter into marriage, which he may do with another girl. One proud bridegroom boasted that he had become a father and a husband on the same day—with different girls. After having had a few children a couple may feel that they trust each other enough to marry. Where a girl has become pregnant, the man will base his decision whether to marry her quite independently of the pregnancy. The fact that she may have had children for other men or may even be pregnant "for" someone else at the time may not be a deterrent. Almost always, men acknowledge their children, and it is no secret in the community who a child's father is. As mentioned, weddings are expensive, but an O.W. child can be supported, with the aid of the Social Welfare Department, for five dollars a month up depending on one's income. Also, the court officials seem quite lenient with fathers in arrears.

To Continentals, natives appear quite tolerant of the extramarital activities of a companion or spouse. As a rule men do not get violently jealous, and they react strongly only if they are teased by other men. While women may verbally abuse a rival, implications of morality do not seem to be involved. It is accepted that men are polygamous, as if this were a biological truth. While women do complain about their husbands, it is generally of their brutality, improvidence, and inconsiderateness rather than of sexual aberration. In general, it is considered bad taste for a woman to talk about her husband's infidelities. Interestingly, they do not bring up the complaint that is so frequent in the States, that husbands are not attentive to children, except in the matter of financial support. A wife does not appear to mind her husband's mistress if the woman is properly deferential to her.[5] A hypothetical question was put by me informally to a number of Continental and native women as to what they would do if they found their husbands unfaithful. The answers from Continental women involved many more threats of retaliation and expressions of hurt pride.

Men in their turn are tolerant of women's accomplishments and are not prejudiced against them in business, government, or the professions. They also seem to pay lip service to the evaluations of them made by women. In 1957 the Women's League sponsored a program on family life. Members, of whom almost all had fulltime jobs, stressed the need for more contact between parents and children and condemned illegitimacy and irresponsible fathers. One woman indignantly accused men of expecting women to work all day and be housemaids in addition. Stimulated by these discussions, a project for a men's group was launched. I was invited to talk to the men at the initial meeting. After listing the various shortcomings of men given by the women, I asked for discussion and contrary opinions. There was unanimous agreement that we had been remiss as husbands and fathers, and resolutions to remedy the situation were made. However, another meeting of the group has never been held.

5. In some departments, unmarried government employees who become pregnant are discharged. One reason for this policy is that the wife of the man involved may work in the same agency and may be subject to taunts by the other woman.

Native Virgin Islanders generally are not prudish about sex; and unchastity, although involving social disapproval, is not viewed as a sin or as the loss of a marketable commodity. However, people are not as outspoken as they were some years ago, when a bill aimed against illegitimacy was brought up in the legislature and an opposing councilman accused the governor of favoring the bill because he, the governor, was impotent! Mothers of girls who become pregnant seem to be more concerned about the deception and flouting of authority than the moral aspects. They are apt to be concerned not with the man having seduced the girl, but with the question of whether he will support the child adequately. The general attitude is that sex is not bad but dangerous.

There is comparatively little differentiation of roles by sex, although this varies with social class. Virgin Islands society is not traditional, so there are few inherited prerogatives. It is not a subsistence culture, so men do not gain prestige as food gatherers. Women are able to support themselves and their families, and the only work that is done exclusively by women is washing and ironing. Nor is there an advanced technology in which superior skill and education give men an advantage over women. In many households men seem superfluous, and many marital problems seem to involve a man not having a significant function in the home and coming off second best in the competition for the child-raising role. An interesting aspect of the lack of differentiation by sex is that there are single hospital wards for men and women.

Because of the absence of the father from many homes and the presumed lack of a male model, it has been suggested that there should be a high incidence of male homosexuality and difficulty in defining the sex role. This does not seem to occur. I encountered the problem only once in a therapeutic situation, and there the attachment involved children. It is obvious that the father's "absence" must be taken in the context of the culture. Homosexuality is not taken seriously in the community but is generally regarded as "foolishness." While it exists, the term does not denote a class of people, a "third sex," nor does it have the extremely derogatory connotations that it has in the continental United States. A recent show of indignation was directed by upper-class, Stateside-educated persons against Continental homosexuals, of whom there is a considerable colony.

Adolescents

Older adolescents do not obtain the identity as a group that teen-agers in the continental United States do. There are few, if any, dressing fads, special argots, modes of dancing, or favored hangouts in drug stores or restaurants. Young people's organizations are adjuncts of adult groups such as the church, and recreation centers for youth have on the whole been unsuccessful. Young unmarried men and women do not have their own residences even if they are self-supporting. Adolescents in the Virgin Islands do not have the traditional role of challenging and criticizing adult authority, and as yet there are no native "beatniks."

Attachments between young people do not seem to be as romanticized as in the States, and courtship is a more practical affair.[6] Girls do not dress in as sexy a fashion

6. Calypso records, popular in the Virgin Islands, do not have any themes of romantic love, despite the many references to sexual activity.

and do not appear as coquettish and seductive as, say, Puerto Ricans. A boy shows interest in a girl by helping her with her schoolwork, making favorable comments on her physical attributes in the presence of others, who are admonished not to tease her, and by boasting about his sexual achievements. Girls respond by asserting their dignity and insulting the boy, but doing nothing to discourage him. Even after the friendship develops, he does not often call for her at home but meets her in the movies or other rendezvous. Girls often prefer the company of older men, and some men "adopt" high school girls, making them gifts in return for sexual favors. If a girl becomes pregnant, the boy is apt to lose interest and go with another girl, but after she has the baby he reappears, proud and boastful. Girls may wear maternity clothes soon after conception, and the attire seems to accentuate rather than conceal the pregnancy. There is considerable concern among boys about their sexual adequacy, that is, their ability to produce babies. The great majority of boys over thirteen have probably had sexual intercourse, and the act is no mystery to the others. Yet despite this, there is great ignorance about the anatomical and physiological aspects of the procreative functions among both adolescents and adults.

Except for those boys and girls who go away to college, adolescence is a brief period without a clear identity, and one passes rapidly from childhood to adult status. In the Virgin Islands, the process is accelerated by the readiness with which youngsters can find jobs that pay as well as most adult occupations. The attaining of motherhood for girls is facilitated in a society where children are easily accepted and provision is made for their care whether born in or out of wedlock. Unlike the situation in the continental United States, youth is not idealized or hailed as the hope of the future, but, instead, young people are expected to assume adult ways.

Psychotic Reactions

The comparative lack of differentiation of social role by sex may be correlated with both the relatively low incidence of sexual themes in psychoses and the character of those hallucinations and delusions that do appear. Virgin Islanders do not structure the environment in terms of sex to the same degree that the French and Continentals do. This does not mean that they are less active sexually in a physical way, but that the biological fact of sex does not determine social role to as great an extent. In psychotic reactions among natives and British Virgin Islanders, sexual ideas were expressed in twelve of ninety cases as compared to twenty-three of the total of fifty-eight French, Puerto Rican, and Continental patients. The difference is more marked when it is noted that sexual delusions in all groups were more common in women, and the French, Puerto Rican, and Continental cases were predominantly male.

The content of the sexual delusions and hallucinations occurring in men seemed to reflect the Virgin Islanders' concern about parenthood. Four men had ideas about sexual impotence and inability to have children. One of them said he was a sexual failure and claimed that he was a virgin even though he had had sexual intercourse. Another heard voices telling him he couldn't have children. Another man said his penis was dead and wanted his sperm tested because it was backing up into his spinal cord and making him weak. The other, a Crucian, was concerned with masculinity and femininity and thought his puffy stomach was making him look like a woman. No one heard voices accusing him of homosexuality or became preoccupied with the subject.

The sexual content of the psychoses occurring in women was characterized by the expression of much hostility toward men. A woman who had been brought to the hospital dressed as a man charged that a broom standing in the cleaning closet would be thrust into her vagina. She also claimed that the nurses were having intercourse with her "husband." Two other women accused men of assaulting them, and here the emphasis seemed to be on violence and attack rather than on sexual intercourse itself. Many of the women were actually sexually aggressive, but sex did not enter into delusions and hallucinations as often as it did in the other cultural groups.

The following case report illustrates the use of sexual symbols in a psychotic reaction. Both this symptomatology and the patriarchal type of family of which the patient was a member are atypical for Virgin Islanders.

CASE REPORT

An eighteen-year old Crucian high school student was admitted to the hospital because of peculiar behavior of five months' duration. He had left school and had refused to go out of the house, claiming that children were laughing at him and that he had heard people calling him a fool. When first interviewed in the out-patient clinic, he said that he had felt badly since inhaling gasoline fumes while doing some work for his father. He also talked in a vague way about not being accepted by his race and said that he had to find somebody white to send him to school in the States. Several months later, he was admitted to the hospital with a fractured ankle after he fell or jumped from a tree.

In the surgical ward, he made an apparent attempt to commit suicide by hanging himself, and psychiatric consultation was requested. He was found reading the Bible and in an ecstatic manner said that God was punishing him for the sin of masturbation. During the next few months he spent a great deal of time masturbating and expressed the idea that he would be killed for this "sin." On the ward he approached both men and women patients with his erect penis exposed, requesting sexual intercourse in a silly, euphoric manner. This behavior alternated with periods of withdrawal and depression in which he spent much of his time sleeping. At these times he also refused food, once commenting, "If I eat food, I'll eat people." He would either deny being ill or would attribute his troubles to a "white woman" (nurse) having given him pills. After some improvement in his behavior, he was allowed to go to stay with and work with his uncle. However, he soon heard God's voice telling him not to work and advising him to have sexual relations with his female cousin.

The patient was the fourth of the eight legitimate children of a sixty-eight-year-old carpenter. The father was also a lay preacher, being known in the community as "The Prophet" and regarded by many as a religious fanatic. His white beard and severe demeanor gave him the appearance of an Old Testament patriarch. In an interview, he denounced doctors as not trusting in God and denied that the patient was ill in any way. He refused to have the patient admitted to the hospital and even after legal commitment would not give consent for any somatic therapy. The father was described by the patient's siblings as a hard worker and good provider, and as extremely strict and dominating in the family. The mother, a native of St. Kitts, was characterized as a very quiet and retiring person, who deferred to her husband. Prior to the onset of his illness, the patient had done well in his school work and had also, at his father's urging, worked after school hours. He had had little interest in girls and his first "dates" had preceded the onset of the illness by several months.

In summary, there is a relative lack of differentiation of social and economic roles of men and women in Virgin Islands culture. As compared with the French, particularly, and to a lesser extent the Puerto Ricans, there is less equating of cultural gender role with biological sex. A Virgin Islander acquires more status through being a parent than as a husband or wife. In psychotic reactions, delusions and hallucinations about sex are infrequent as compared with the incidence in the other cultural groups under study.

4   PARENT-CHILD
RELATIONSHIPS

NATIVE VIRGIN ISLANDERS and Tortolans
derive a great deal of identity through the parent-child relationship. Through their children they structure much of
their experience, express many of their needs, and are able
to formulate their feelings in a particularly meaningful
fashion. This way of interacting in the environment far
transcends the fulfillment of instinctive or biological
drives. The parent-child relationship is the most significant
interpersonal transaction in Virgin Islands society, and
the symbol of a child, particularly a small, helpless one,
is an area of language through which a wide range of
reality is conceived. This involves not only the child-
raising situation itself, but also patterns of adult relationships. Under conditions of stress, ranging from everyday encounters to the psychoses, a Virgin Islander's

identity is affirmed in terms of the cultural values that cluster about children.

Child-raising Patterns

The aim of the very great majority of native Virgin Islands parents is to raise their children to be respectable and well behaved. A child is expected to be quiet, decorous, truthful, and obedient at an early age. The terms "rude" and "disgusting" generally apply to a noisy or very active child. A school principal listed slovenliness, boisterous behavior, and disobedience as the main offenses of elementary school students. Children sit quietly in clinics, offices, and church without touching, exploring, "fussing," and interrupting adult conversation, in striking contrast to their stateside counterparts. Respect for the grown-up members of the family is demanded, though no longer to the extent that a child will be whipped for failure to say good morning to an older relative or family friend. In many ways children are expected to conform to adult standards of politeness.

Discipline is exercised in an arbitrary fashion and punishment for a seemingly trivial offense may be as severe as for a serious one. Whipping is cited by informants as the standard form of punishment. It is difficult to gauge how much whipping is actually done or exactly what degree of slapping or cuffing is necessary to constitute a whipping. Although whippings are generally administered with a belt or strap, they are rarely severe. The one whipping I saw had a highly ludic character. A father chased a boy into a field with a large strap, and the performance was watched by a highly amused audience of a half-dozen children. Edith Clarke, writing of Jamaica, feels that whipping is a sort of ritual in which the parent relieves his own anxiety. Severe beatings of children occur more commonly among Tortolans. Mr. Jarvis told me the story of a Tortolan father who would appear at monthly intervals to whip his three children on the premise that if they had not deserved it in the previous month, they might in subsequent weeks.

Disapproval is also communicated by scolding, threatening, and certain nonverbal gestures, of which silence and tooth-sucking may be the most characteristic. Children are not often praised, as this is thought to spoil them. Although punishment is readily administered, parents take offense when another adult corrects their child. Scoldings and punishments by teachers are also apt to be resented by parents.

Physical aggression on the part of children is viewed with strong disapproval. Actually, it is not common and aggressive acts are rather directed at dogs, donkeys, dolls, and toys. There is very little of the attitude, common in the States, of urging a boy to "fight his own battles." There is much concern over juvenile delinquency although it does not exist in the Islands in the form of destructive acts by organized gangs. Delinquency is rather expressed in acts of omission like truancy from school and wandering off and not returning at night. Adults complain of lack of respect to grown-ups, the defacing of white walls, and stone throwing.[1] One hears

1. Stone throwing carries particular connotations of disrespect and contempt. The mother of a boy who had been disturbed for a long time finally brought him to the hospital when he threw stones at a neighbor and she was afraid of being talked about. In Jamaica,

much talk of the old Danish days when whippings were given in the Fort and a gendarme's look was usually enough to discourage any youthful "foolishness."

Young children are indulged, and receive a great amount of physical affection. Babies are admired, fondled, petted, and carried about, baby carriages and strollers not being used. At times it seems as if a baby is treated as an elaborate toy. In the early years, upbringing is lenient and only children are more apt to be "spoiled." Generally, children are weaned early and mothers are not strict about particular foods or regularity of meals. The matter of breast feeding versus bottle feeding furnishes a good example of the way parent-child relationships are shaped by the requirements of parental prestige. Bottle feeding is regarded as much the superior American way, with the advertisements of condensed milk companies illustrating the fashion. Native Virgin Islands nurses insist that French and Puerto Rican mothers bottle-feed their babies, even though the home surroundings make the sterilization of bottles practically impossible. Parents, especially in lower-class homes, are casual about toilet training. Young children spend most of their time outdoors wearing little clothing, so the performance of urinary and bowel functions is considered to be a simple matter. Upper-class families tend to be somewhat stricter in their toilet training. Pacifiers are used a great deal, and thumb sucking is not uncommon. Parents are not prudish about letting little children run about the house with little or nothing on, but the matter of clothing is important when the child is taken out. It then is dressed

---

there is a superstition that the spirits of the dead throw stones. Thus, the pockets of clothes are cut before burial to prevent a supply from being carried about by the spirits.

with a great deal of care and expense, with much time spent on grooming its hair. Children under six are not expected to dress themselves, as the emphasis is on having the child look well. Even poor families are lavish with the money and time spent in dressing up children, who are brought to clinic often in their best and fanciest clothes. One doctor calls the well-baby clinic in St. Croix a "fashion show."

As a child grows older, he tends to receive less attention, and the process is accelerated by the arrival of another baby in the household. As he becomes more autonomous and capable of expressing himself, he meets with more restrictions. Whereas previously he has been indulged and even spoiled, now independent behavior is arbitrarily curbed. The situation is more acute with boys in a home in which there are only, or mainly, women. Often an older woman, who is living alone or whose children are grown, takes a child to keep herself from becoming lonely, and to have help with the chores. Such homes generally have very limited facilities for the expression of the interests of boys, and situations arise where the adult complains of the child's rebelliousness and "rudeness" and brings him to the court, a minister, or even the psychiatrist for disciplining. A fair number of the admissions to the Insular Training School for Boys arise out of such relationships. The following case abstract is illustrative of some of these social factors:

CASE REPORT

A nine-and-a-half year old boy was brought for psychiatric examination because of truancy and vagrancy. He was the eldest of five children whom his mother had borne "for" three men. She stated that, while recognizing that

Ronald needed a man in the home, she had never married because Ronald's father had died and her last companion had married someone else because she "had too many children." The father of two of the children had lived in the home for a time, but the informant said he had been too harsh with, and intolerant of, the children. When Ronald was four, he had gone to live with his godmother because she was lonely without children in the home. The mother stated that Ronald was spoiled, and when he became unruly at the age of eight, his godmother returned him and took his younger and better-behaved brother to live with her.

Ronald's mother complained that he would wander off while she was at work and not come home in the evening. She did not believe he was disobedient and resentful but said he was secretive (the social worker noted that Ronald would go off when the mother was not at home). The mother also complained that she could not trust Ronald with the baby. He was very fond of the child, but would "hug and squeeze him too tight." The mother felt that she could not cope with Ronald and was eager to have him admitted to the Training School.

Girls often seem to fit in better with the activities of the household, but there is not much differentiation of actual duties on the basis of sex difference. Girls do more chores inside the house, but boys will do some cooking, washing, and ironing, and one sees boys as well as girls carrying water. Boys do resent tasks that seem to infringe on prestige. Thus, they will mop the floor but dislike doing it on their knees. In general, boys are not preferred over girls and do not derive special status by reason of sex.

In contrast to rigidity in other matters, parents and guardians are generally permissive about eating. They are not at all strict about particular foods or the regularity of mealtimes. In St. Thomas, particularly, eating is a rather casual operation in which family members may eat separately at various places in and out of the house. Relatively young children of both sexes may prepare their own food while adults are busy. In this pattern the absence of refrigeration and lack of utensils and space are important factors, but even among upper-class persons meals are very apt to be informal. I once asked a lower-class mother what she fed her child. She answered "what he likes" in a manner that clearly indicated her surprise at the question. In St. Croix, families are more likely to eat together, and food is a more important element in parent-child relationships. It is of interest that feeding problems are more commonly reported in St. Croix than in St. Thomas or St. John.

Work is not assigned in the home as a means of character training and for inculcating habits of industry and responsibility.[2] Chores are given because the work is necessary to the household, and the evaluation is of the efficiency rather than in the appreciation of the effort in itself, recognizing that children cannot be judged by adult standards. Families who employ servants regard children's jobs as an imposition and even as a reflection on their ability to care properly for the children. Play is not ordinarily thought of as useful in a child's development and is not encouraged. Rather, a child may be cautioned about getting his clothes dirty. Children are not given money allowances as a form of training. Rather,

2. Virgin Islanders are highly amused by the pride taken by American parents in the paper routes of their sons and by stories of how a mother will fill in if some other activity of the child supervenes. It would be rare for a Virgin Islander to put in the long hours of work demanded of a "den mother" in the States.

they are apt to be given money when they request it for a specific purpose, like going to the movies. God-mothers and other relatives are likely to be very generous with gifts, finding it difficult to refuse a child. Some children find in O.W. fathers a convenient source of occasional revenue.

The judging of children by adult standards and the arbitrary insistence on abstracted qualities of behavior such as obedience and honesty can be readily observed in school situations. In a study of adult-child communication in a kindergarten group of two teachers and fifty pupils of mainly lower-class origin, Joy Schulterbrandt noted that there was little interaction between teachers and children unless someone misbehaved or made a mistake. Teachers acted mainly as disciplinarians, enforcing proper behavior through scolding, shaming, and occasional corporal punishment. On one occasion ten cents were missing from a fund collected among the children. Although the teacher knew the culprit, she had each child in turn remove his shoes and socks until the money was found in the guilty one's shoe. The child's mother was then notified. When a child cried, the incident was joked about or he was told to stop because there was nothing wrong with him. There were no physical manifestations of affection or sympathy such as embracing a child. When praise was given, it was less often done so directly than by talking favorably of the child to others, and when a child made a mistake he was frequently chided for his ignorance.

In school there is little effort made to encourage creative activity and fantasy. In a comparison of the grade school attended by native children with a kindergarten group of Continental and upper-class native children,

Miss Schulterbrandt found that only the latter talked of "imaginary companions" or made up stories of fancied happenings. In the group of native children, no stories were told by teachers to which a child could respond in kind. Children spent most of their time in relatively unsupervised play, which among girls was largely imitation of household activities like ironing. There was also a great deal of reciting in unison of such things as the day of the week and the date of the month, with no apparent thought of how the material fitted into the child's scheme of reality.

It seemed that the meaning for the child was determined more by the way the vocal and other physical aspects of the experience made him part of the group than what the content of the recitation meant in relation to the "real" world. Dr. Elsa Walters, speaking of elementary school education in the British Caribbean, comments that the world of the schoolroom exists quite independently from that derived from the child's experience outside of it. She tells of a class of boys who wrote, "I am a little girl," when asked to write who they were, because having seen this written on the blackboard they assumed it was the correct answer.

Native Virgin Islands children do not progress as rapidly in school nor do as well on intelligence tests as do children of Continental background.[3] Along with the factors of economic position, social class, educational level of parents, and the adequacy of instruction by teachers, some aspects of enculturation appear significant. Children in a testing situation appear quite frightened of

3. According to Dr. Alain Plénel, Superintendent of Schools in Martinique, children there perform at the same level as do those in metropolitan France.

making a mistake, and become inarticulate. They do not accept the test as a sort of game and generally will not guess at an answer lest it be wrong and the child appear ridiculous. I noted that many six- and seven-year-old children were having difficulty in distinguishing their left and right hands and conceptualizing the right-left relationship in other contexts. After I heard one mother scold a youngster for putting on the "wrong" shoe after an examination, I felt that such a child must learn early in life to get the right answer by knowing which shoe was which through some physical characteristic of the objects such as a scuff or a stain. He does not have much of an opportunity to "play" in his environment by, say, putting on a shirt wrong side out, from which he can derive a broader concept of spatial relationships.

Another cultural factor related to test performance came up during an enquiry into poor performance on the "absurdities" section of one of the standard intelligence tests. Children are shown pictures of such things as a donkey with one ear or a chair with three legs and are asked what is wrong with the picture. A number of children who had said there was nothing "wrong" explained that someone might have cut off the donkey's ear or broken off the chair leg. In American culture we tacitly assume that if something isn't working properly, it *should* be, whereas such unconsciously operating assumptions are not necessarily made by others.

The play of young children in the Virgin Islands seems to consist of rushing about, shouting, various types of hitting games, and, for boys, imitations of cowboys with guns. Jarvis notes that they particularly like to play with water, possibly because rainfall is so scant and there are no running streams. The year-round sunny weather[4] and the small, crowded houses are factors in the predominance of such outdoor activity. Children do not generally play at such indoor pastimes as puzzles or parcheesi and other dice games, which develop skill in arithmetic and the appreciation of time-space relationships. Only recently have children been encouraged to read for pleasure rather than only for proficiency in school. Jarvis comments that Virgin Islands children are not collectors of shells, stamps, insects, and such; and thus they do not enter into these worlds of romantic names and associations.

Parents in all classes of native families are eager for their children to do well in school, although as a rule they are not interested in the actual school work or activities. At a community discussion of parent-child relationships, a speaker commented that, while parents do not like to attend P.T.A. meetings, they move heaven and earth should a child's card show poor marks. Expulsion of a child from school may even lead to a protest to the governor. While there are a few organizations for children, such as the scouts, modeled on those in the States, adults generally do not take upon themselves the necessary chores involved in furthering such activities. Aside from the schools, children's organizations are generally part of an adult group such as the church or the festivities of carnivals.

There is much anxiety over the health and safety of children among native Virgin Islanders. There is a large attendance at clinics, and children are often brought in with trivial complaints, so that the hospital treats a great

4. Someone, speaking of the Mediterranean, said the weather was good and the climate was bad. This is certainly true of the Virgin Islands.

many "emergencies" and "bad feelings." (The policy of the government is to treat children without fee, and one is a child until the age of twenty-one; 99 per cent of births occur in the hospitals.) There is an almost universal belief that one will catch cold if exposed to rain. Children may even be truants from school to go to a doctor, and it is the custom of parents to bring them in on a Saturday for a "check-up." Programs of prophylactic inoculation are highly successful and even overeagerly supported. Parents may not be satisfied with an immune reaction to a vaccination but insist on coming in until a "take" is recorded. Yet when parents are confronted with a serious illness, they may become panicky and refuse to let a child enter the hospital. Many superstitions about health persist, such as taking care that an ill person doesn't breathe on a child; and present-day miracle drugs and "shots" seem to have taken the place of the magical procedures of the past. Bed wetting is common but does not seem to be a concern of parents. In a psychiatric clinic the only children brought in for treatment of enuresis were those of Continentals or Puerto Ricans.

Religion plays a large part in the raising of children in that religious practises and beliefs are elements of proper behavior. Many parents consider the teaching of respect, manners, and the Bible as the most important components of child training. Obedience and polite behavior are thought of as Christian values that are pleasing to God. I complimented one woman on how diligently her ten-year-old daughter said her prayers. She replied, "She better or she get a licking." While such active methods of enforcement are most prevalent in Tortolan and lower-class native families, there is a general tendency to equate the will of God with parental authority.

Ideas of Children Symbolizing Adult Attitudes

The behavior of children is very much a matter of parental prestige, however unaware parents may be of the degree to which they express their own needs through their children. "Rude" conduct in a child or criticism of a child by others is regarded as a reflection on parents. Children are forbidden to have neighborhood playmates whose families are disapproved. Parents are more upset if children fight with outsiders than with their siblings. Parents are very eager to have their children confirmed in church, but after confirmation the great majority of children, in the Protestant churches at least, no longer attend. Several years ago special classes for slow learners in the schools were set up, but parents refused to co-operate because they felt that a child who went to the school would be stigmatized as stupid.

One frequently hears the expression, "Virgin Islanders love children," and this is borne out by the great desire of both women and men to have children, the interest expressed by parents in children's welfare, the concern about their health, and the sentimental feelings expressed about them. Islanders will accept almost any child in the home, while Puerto Ricans are apt to insist that the child they take in be a blood relative. It is of interest that there does not seem to be any problem of sterility, or at least women do not seek medical advice if they have not borne children. It appears as if the biological act of child bearing is not essential for the feeling of motherhood. Older women who feel lonely[5] take a child to live

5. Madeleine Kerr states that in Jamaica a lonely old person is called an "orphan."

with them. They may select a grandchild, or a niece or nephew of whom they are particularly fond. It is not uncommon for a woman to sleep with the youngest child in the home. A mother may "give away" a child to a friend or relative out of sympathy or friendship. One woman told of having given a child to her godmother out of gratitude for having been brought up herself. Sometimes, though, a mother who has neglected her children may refuse to have them placed in a home because this will reflect on her as a mother.

Children are also the vehicle for the expression of negative feelings. For example, adults may express resentment by mistreating the favorite child of someone that they do not like. In homes where there are children of several fathers, a mother may take out her feelings toward the father on his child. Some upper-class parents are fearful of sending their children to the public schools, lest a teacher of lower social standing should take out her envy on the child. Yet there is a tremendous denial among Virgin Islanders that an adult can have hostile feelings toward a child. In a seminar of community leaders on the subject of parent-child communication, the question of how adults might communicate hate and attitudes of rejection was brought up. A number of the participants refused to discuss the issue as they felt it was impossible for a grown-up to hate a child!

There are some interesting comparisons between the attitudes of Continental and native mothers who bring children to the Mental Health Clinic for behavior problems. Many of the Continental women have been so influenced by the articles in popular magazines and the pronouncements of experts on child raising that they begin an interview with expressions of guilt and apologies for having made mistakes or having read the wrong child-rearing manuals. Native mothers, on the other hand, are generally quite certain that the difficulty lies in the child being "willful," "hardheaded," or "off his head." They usually have little doubt that they have brought the child up correctly and are often quite open in saying that the child should be sent to the Insular School because they cannot stand the "harassment."

Concern about children is sometimes the means whereby parents seek psychiatric help for themselves. The following case is illustrative:

CASE REPORT

A forty-eight-year-old hotel maid brought her eleven-year-old grandson, Regis, to the clinic expressing a fear that he might die in his sleep. She began her description of the boy by saying that he was a frightful (fearful) child and one that "can't be bawled at." She said Regis had been a premature baby, weighing four pounds at birth, and a doctor had told her that he had a heart murmur. She then talked of the child's difficulties in school in the context of teachers being "wrothful" with him to the point where she had gotten so mad that she had gone straight to the governor. After this initial account of the child's behavior she began to talk of her own troubles, her headaches, her difficulties in sleeping, and the fear that she would die. She had had several previous psychotic episodes and felt that people held it against her because she had been crazy.

After several interviews and medication, the patient improved in that she no longer had headaches, was sleeping well, and did not feel worried about Regis. She began her next visit with the rather casual announcement of the death of a seven-months-old grandchild, who had come down with her daughter to visit her. While the child's mother had cried, she stated she had felt calm in the assurance that "the Lord giveth and the Lord taketh away." She then described how Regis and the mother had cried over the dead child.

The patient resolved her own fears through the symbol of a child in danger of death. When another child actually died, she was less upset and was able to adapt effectively to the loss through religious language.

People who seemed otherwise quite inarticulate were able to express their feelings and relate experiences in the symbolism of children, and in the following case also through the representation of the violence of men:

CASE REPORT

A sixteen-year-old girl was seen because of headaches and depressive episodes. She had left school because of "bad tonsils and a run-down condition" associated with an O.W. pregnancy. After the birth of the baby, her health was said to have improved for a time. The patient lived with her mother, eight siblings, and her grandmother. The grandmother took care of the patient's baby because the patient's mother herself had recently had a child "for" a companion. In the first interview, the patient responded to the initial question as to her symptoms with a description of how her baby was always sick. In referring to her headaches she described them as coming on after her boy friend had hit her on the head with a rock. The girl generally appeared tense and taciturn and seemed to be able to talk of her everyday doings in terms of her child and the brutality of men. She would tell of what the baby had done, how worried she was about its health, and how it followed her about. She frequently brought the baby in and held it in her lap. When asked about her relationship with her mother, she told of how the mother had taken care of her when she was a small, sickly baby (the truth was that the mother, who was fifteen at the time of her birth, had not taken care of her). In one session she was depressed and uncommunicative throughout, becoming animated only when announcing that the baby had had its first birthday. In the course of therapy she got married and introduced the news by mentioning that her husband had beaten her.

The symbolism of children, particularly little, helpless ones is commonly used in everyday language. It serves to sharpen emotional impact and to make experience more vivid and meaningful. In stress, such symbols tend to give a feeling of versimilitude to excuses, rationalization and justifications, and even confabulations. A minister commented that he could express himself to his congregation most empathically in parables of children. Speeches regularly liken Virgin Islands institutions to infants. Following a recent devastating flood, a rumor spread in the community that a child had been drowned. At a conference of the staff of a large government department, the question of the moving of offices from the main building was taken up. An official who felt that he was being stripped of some authority objected to the change because "children going to the new office would get wet in the rain." A young man was on trial because he had shot and wounded his girl friend and her father after the father had forbidden him to see her. He explained that he had shot Mr. H because "he wasn't good to his children." Then, believing the father was dead, he stated that he shot the girl "because she would be so lonesome as an orphan."

It is common for men wishing to feel secure in stressful or unfamiliar circumstances to initiate conversation by telling how many children they have and how generous they are to them. When native Virgin Islands patients on the psychiatric ward ask for permission to leave the hospital, they commonly give as the reason having to take care of their children, buying a godchild a gift, finding a place for children to live, and so forth. In contrast, Puerto Ricans characteristically have to go to work, the French insist they are not crazy, and a Continental is likely to have a business deal about which he must see his lawyer immediately.

Out-of-Wedlock Pregnancy

Together with economic, social, and legal factors, the symbolic significance of children is germane to the issue of the young unmarried mother and, to some extent, of the unmarried father. O.W. pregnancy cannot be explained simply on the basis of promiscuity or ignorance of the facts of procreation. While there are no Kinsey-type statistics for the Virgin Islands, a teen-aged mother may not have had sexual intercourse any more frequently than a girl who avoids pregnancy. Some seem to have become pregnant after their first coitus. Most Virgin Islands children, growing up as they do in crowded quarters, have witnessed the sexual act. Contraceptives are sold in great numbers. Nor is pregnancy simply an unfortunate, accidental complication of romance. Rather, the pregnancy involves a positive need to have a baby, and the prospect of impregnation may act as a stimulus rather than a deterrent to sexual intercourse.

A psychiatrist is more apt to see unmarried mothers from the more economically deprived homes and thus encounters a high proportion of girls with emotional problems. Yet the over-all impression is that the young O.W. mother is not a rebellious or independent person who is expressing resentment against her family. Rather, she seems quite immature and dependent on her mother or other female relatives. Through having the baby, she achieves feelings of love and security and at the same time increases her dependence. If she has been lost in a shuffle of siblings, she now becomes the center of attention. Several girls first formed an attachment for the boy's mother, and the desire to live with her may have been an inducement to become pregnant. It is of interest that some young women with known homosexual attachments have had a number of O.W. children. The young mother may be regarded as gaining identity through her baby and in this way experiencing feelings of love. In taking the roles of both mother and baby, she recaptures the most significant interpersonal relationship in the culture. It may not be surprising that the mother loses interest in the child as he gets older and is no longer a mere vehicle for the implementing of feelings of love.

Some of the dependent and immature attitudes of young girls who repeatedly have O.W. children are illustrated in the following case abstract:

CASE REPORT

A twenty-one-year-old girl, Melitta, was brought to the hospital by her mother for repeated temper outbursts and for throwing stones into the crib of her two-year-old nephew. Melitta lived with her mother, her two O.W. children, Darlene and Cerise, four-and-one-half and one-and-one-half, her mother, two brothers, an uncle, and her sister and sister's son. She had become pregnant with the elder child while in the tenth grade "for" a boy of eighteen who was in the ninth grade. The boy joined the

Army and after his return she had another child "for" him. The father supports the children but Melitta says that she does not want to marry him because he is "no good" and "brutal." She quotes him as telling her that he has other girls and claiming that he has not had enough fun yet. She does not feel badly about not being married because her mother was never married, and a sister, who went to New York, had an O.W. child. Melitta's mother had three children by one man and five by another. As a baby, Melitta lived with the daughters of her godmother, joining her mother when she was seven.

Melitta feels that her mother has been quarrelsome with her since her first child was born. She claims that her mother favors the two-year-old nephew just because he is from the States. She also charged that her sister knocked Darlene and Cerise. The mother states that Melitta feels that no one likes her, that she spends much of her time lying in bed, and that she shows little interest in her children.

O.W. pregnancies are often encouraged tacitly by a mother, grandmother, or guardian. While a mother may warn the girl about having intercourse with men, she herself may be the mother of several O.W. children. Mothers sometimes seem to accept older or married men visitors whose intentions might seem quite obvious. When pregnancy results, there may be an initial storm, but after that the girl and baby are accepted. The attitude is that extramarital sexual relations are not so much wrong as dangerous, and the mother may be more incensed over the girl's disobedience and the challenge to her authority than over the fall from virtue. One particularly indignant mother, who had had six O.W. children for three men, brought her sixteen-year-old daughter to the hospital "to have her virginity tested." She had warned the girl against going with a truck driver, as she was certain the man would not support the baby. The girl became pregnant not long after, and one gets the feeling that she was only doing what Mother wanted her to do. In another case, a girl had become pregnant "for" a bus driver as a consequence of an unscheduled stop. When the mother discovered the pregnancy, she first abused the girl severely for deceiving her. She then suggested that the girl might continue to have intercourse with the man, as this would make the delivery easier. In the case of an unmarried, mentally ill girl, who had had two O.W. children, a welfare worker suggested that her condition might be benefited by allowing her to get pregnant again.

The question of whether an unmarried mother feels ashamed or embarrassed is a complex one. Girls are aware of the official disapproval of the community, and students who become pregnant are expelled from school. Girls may deny their pregnancy when confronted by employers, doctors, or welfare workers. Yet, as has been mentioned, the custom is to wear maternity clothes early,[6] in some cases, right after conception. For a girl who feels deprived and inferior anyway, the additional disapproval of others may not matter particularly, and she may then relieve the added anxiety by getting pregnant again. It is likely that the feelings of security generated by the pregnancy may outweigh any lasting effects of censure. Pregnancies of unmarried mothers are not accompanied by any more psychosomatic symptoms than are present in married women. An "unlawful" child may feel inferior,

6. This may be related to the belief that wearing tight clothes may harm the baby.

especially if there are legitimate children in the home. Yet the same boy may also feel proud of the many children, legitimate and otherwise, that his father may have. Such seemingly contradictory attitudes may reflect the ambivalent feelings of the community. While O.W. pregnancy is deplored, abortion would be considered to be much worse. There is also the widespread belief that having a baby is necessary to a woman's health and that a woman is destined to have a certain number of children.

Psychotic Reactions

The symbolism of children is prominent under conditions of great stress such as occur in severe emotional disturbances and psychotic reactions. Thus, one woman, on her conversion to an "outside" church, signalized the repentance of her sins by putting her O.W. child out of the home. The early symptoms of psychoses may involve changes in behavior toward children. One young married woman developed an obsessive preoccupation with her children's clothes, which was followed by her refusing to let them go out of the house during the day and constantly picking them up at night. When she used obscene language to her grandmother, she was hospitalized. In the initial interview she appeared preoccupied but answered most questions promptly. She stated that there was nothing the matter with her; and when asked if she had seen a doctor prior to admission, she stated only that the doctor had come to check her daughter for a head cold. Her only spontaneous statement was a remark that she was thinking of Jellice (her elder child). In this case, the patient seemed able to depict her experience and symbolize her fears about herself only in terms of her children.

Another woman developed a great worry that the seats in school were not clean enough for her two children and got into an altercation with the teachers over it. She then withdrew the boys from school, and, according to the neighbors, refused to have their hair cut, spending much time in grooming it. After being hospitalized, she went into a long, rambling monologue about the policeman trying to grab her child (actually the patient had resisted coming to the hospital and was referring to the officer's efforts to bring her). Another mother of four came to the attention of the authorities because she roamed the streets at all hours with her two younger children. She claimed that she was looking for her two elder children. They were actually in the States, but the patient insisted that she had seen them. The first overt delusion of another woman was that children were sleeping in her bed, were in charge of the house, and had stolen a charm from her. This patient would sit by a vent in her house addressing it as "little boy." Another case was of a woman who after each of several pregnancies had psychotic episodes in which she threatened to kill her children and drown herself.

In classifying the content of the delusions and hallucinations of psychotic patients, it was found that in native Virgin Islanders and Tortolans the theme of children was very commonly used, occurring in thirty-one of ninety cases, while in the French and Puerto Ricans it appeared only rarely (twice in fifty-eight cases). The difference is not actually as great when it is noted that delusions about children are much more common in women, who make up more than half of the Virgin Islands group and less than one-third of the others. In both men and women hallucinations took the form of seeing children or hearing their voices. One man who had been suspicious of his wife's fidelity claimed that a "child" had found a man under her bed, while a woman heard a voice telling her to take her children out of the house. Several women and one man expressed the idea that they were pregnant or had given birth to a child in the hospital. One woman reported a vision of having seen a blind child on the altar in church. Frequently there was a delusion or confabulation that a child had been killed or injured. An old lady claimed that her grandson had killed a child and would be arrested, while a severely depressed young woman insisted that there were five dead babies in her valise. In the few depressive reactions in which feelings of unworthiness were expressed, they concerned children, as in the case of the young woman who said she had sinned by having an abortion performed.

The following case report is illustrative of the way delusions and dreams about children appear as condensed representations of one's own disturbed interpersonal relationships.

CASE REPORT

A twenty-three-year-old girl, a native of Tortola, was admitted to the hospital in an acutely agitated, screaming state. She shouted about God and Jesus and insisted that she was having a baby. She was disoriented for place, saying that she was in Roadtown (Tortola) because the women on the ward were wearing English dresses. She was briefly assaultive, misidentified a janitor as her husband, and accused the nurse of scheming against her. After her agitated state subsided with the administration of tranquilizers, she became withdrawn and expressed thoughts about being dead. Clinical improvement began about a week after admission, though she still maintained that she was pregnant. This was followed by asking if she had lost the baby, and she began to talk about how her mother had beaten her when she was pregnant with her first (and only) child. She also complained about the woman for whom she had worked, saying that her hours had been too long and that her mistress had said bad things, which made other girls from Tortola laugh at her. For the last week of her three-week hospitalization she did not express any critical feelings. She acted in a reserved, dignified manner spending much time reading the Bible. Her plan was to visit with her mother-in-law in Tortola to rest. Shortly before discharge she had the following dream: "I had a baby and J (her six-year old child) burned the baby with a goose ("goose" means clothes iron) and the clothes were sticking to the burned place."

The patient had come from Tortola five years previously when her child was one year old. Several months after the child's birth she had had a similar, brief psychotic episode brought on presumably by the father's refusal to marry her. She had worked as a domestic until her marriage two-and-one-half months prior to the present illness, and at the time of her marriage she had left to take a job at the establishment where her husband worked. The patient and her mistress had had a close, tutelary relationship. The latter told later of her disappointment over the secrecy that had attended the events leading to the patient's marriage.

Though the loss of a "mother-daughter" type relationship is not necessarily the cause of this psychotic reaction, the patient appears to be representing her feelings of loneliness and unhappiness in symbols of an unborn child, a lost child, a burned child, and an unloving mother.

In the following case, while delusions were not prominent, "pregnancy addiction" was an outstanding feature of a series of psychotic episodes.

CASE REPORT

Alita was thirty years old and her most recent hospital admission had been caused by her drinking and overactive, menacing behavior at home in which she had cursed and assaulted her parents, beaten her two year old child, and bitten her brother when he tried to protect her child. When first seen she was in her seventh or eighth pregnancy. She presented her problems in autobiographical fashion. She was the youngest child and only girl among four. Prior to her birth her mother had had numerous miscarriages but had persisted in becoming pregnant because she had always wanted a girl. At the age of fourteen, Alita had an illness that left her with a back deformity, and the patient dated all of her subsequent difficulties from this time. Prior to it her parents had loved her a great deal and she described how tenderly they had nursed her while she was ill. Afterwards, she said, they had pitied her so much that she was taken out of school so that she would not be teased. The patient also felt that her parents had become more strict with her in order that the other children not take advantage of her.

Her first psychotic episode occurred when she was eighteen. This was attributed to slowness of menstruation, the blood traveling to her head. She then felt that she needed to have a child and according to her parents she became promiscuous, usually with married men. Alita's interpretation was that her parents did not want her to get married and forbade suitors to come to the house. Her second episode came at twenty. She felt that she was going crazy and harassed a fellow until he got her pregnant. She knew right after intercourse that she was pregnant because she felt so much better. She further justified her need for children by commenting that she came from a "breeding family." It was actually difficult to learn how many pregnancies she had had because she frequently had claimed to be, and walked and dressed as if she were.

In the hospital she talked loudly to unseen people, particularly berating the absent father of the child she was carrying. She worried that her own two children might be mistreated and eat worms and dirt. She blamed her hospitalization on her brother's drunkenness, saying that he had "disrespected" her parents and instead of spoiling him they should drive him from the home. She said the brother was in danger of dying but had been afraid of seeing the doctor (giving the name of the physician who had previously treated her). Her agitated state subsided in a few days after which she had no complaints except that the baby would get frightened by noises and send shocks through her body. She was contrite over the lack of respect toward her parents and told of her fears of dying, and how she had prayed that God would get her to the hospital in time.

On her next admission, the patient was depressed, tearful, and complained of weakness and insomnia. She expressed guilt that she had done bad things, sinned in the sight of God, and abused her parents. Whereas on previous admissions she had worked and entered into ward activities despite her disturbed condition, she now lay about in dispirited fashion. On this admission she did not talk about pregnancy or children.

Her final hospital admission was precipitated by threatening behavior to her children and parents. She was in an excited, exalted state and was hostile to the staff. She demanded to go home so she could take care of her children. She approached male patients sexually. She told a nurse, "All the men up here wants to sex with me and it's time for me to have another baby. My mother had twenty children and I want to have forty. I'm a sex maniac but I'm not crazy because crazy people fight and tear each other up." After a week she became quiet and said that she needed a child or else she would go crazy. She thought she might have been made pregnant by one of the patients. She was particularly eager to be home for her child's birthday.

5 OTHER INTERPERSONAL RELATIONSHIPS: FEARS AND HOSTILITIES

THIS CHAPTER will describe social transactions other than those determined by sex and the parent-child relationship and will take up how status is defined in the course of such relationships. It will also consider how fears and hostilities are integrated into symbolic patterns and how such patterns, as well as the content of psychotic delusions, may serve as modes of adaptation to stress. Eating as a social process will be discussed, with particular reference to the difference between St. Thomians and Crucians.

Social Transactions

While there is a great deal of difficulty in making objective determinations of social class, Virgin Islanders, especially persons in the upper class, are very "class

conscious." This involves the obtaining of overt manifestations of deference from those considered to be be-
neath one in the social scale. It is important to note, for
example, who greets whom first on the street. While
upper-class persons no longer feel ashamed to be seen
carrying a bundle on the street, the maintenance of an
appearance of dignity is of great moment. Some people
feel quite insulted if they are jostled on the narrow,
crowded streets of Charlotte Amalie on the days of cruise
boat visits. (It was in reference to such attitudes that
an official of the local tourist board advised natives to
"think of tourists as if they were walking dollar bills.")
Continentals have observed that some natives will emphasize their upper-class status by being particularly
peremptory with servants and waiters.

The clothing that one wears is so important a factor
in the maintenance of prestige among Virgin Islanders
as to merit a separate paragraph. Under the Danes, a
white linen suit was practically the badge of the ruling
class. It is said that shopkeepers would not sell a lower-
class person clothing or material that they felt her status
did not warrant. The pride in dressing children well has
been mentioned, and people go to great pains and expense for beautiful and elaborate costumes for carnivals
and school plays. In the hospital, native doctors dress
with more style and formality than their Continental col-
leagues. A child may not be sent to school if his parents
do not consider him adequately dressed, and a maid
may not go on an errand until she changes to proper
clothes. The disgrace felt in going barefoot is so great
that taking patients' shoes from them is an effective
means of preventing elopements from the psychiatric
ward. Several years ago, some members of the Women's

League were disturbed over the "short shorts" worn by women tourists, feeling that such attire betokened scorn and disrespect for the local community. A mother may warn a child about being run over by cars by admonishing her to wear clean underpants in case she has to be taken to the hospital and examined. People with very low income may spend a great proportion of it on clothes.[1] While great care is taken with dress and usually with personal cleanliness, this does not apply to houses. Or if homes are well kept within, there may be beer cans and other litter scattered outside.

There is much sensitivity to criticism and implications of disrespect, and people in general are fearful of slights and ridicule. Teachers working with adolescents comment on how upset they become when corrected. A worker may even quit a well-paying job if he is spoken to rudely, and this attitude causes problems on construction jobs where there are Continental foremen and native laborers. It is important for a customer or an employer to phrase requests and orders in a courteous and properly polite fashion. If a waiter feels that he has been treated with disrespect or addressed in a peremptory way, he may ignore the customer, regardless of the sacrifice of a prospective tip. In describing such attitudes Campbell (1943) commented that "St. Thomians wear their feelings on their sleeves."

Virgin Islanders, especially St. Thomians, do not accept authority readily. For instance, a policeman enforcing a traffic regulation may be "told off" with a remark to

1. Many lower-class people regard money as a kind of luxury. They live in an economy where shelter needs are minimal and food is shared or little eaten. Continental shopkeepers comment that people do not question high prices, but buy if they have the money.

the effect that "slavery was abolished in 1848." A few
years ago, a taxi driver refused to move from his place
in line to let the governor's official car through. This attitude is complemented by an unwillingness to assume
responsibility and give orders to other persons for fear
of incurring their resentment. An important factor in
such attitudes is that in a small community like St. Thomas
people have known each other or of each other for many
years. Also it reflects the derivation of identity through
personal relationships rather than in terms of ethnic
group, caste, or occupation.

Among Virgin Islanders, there seems to be a great
expectation of being blamed for something. People will
not admit even trivial mistakes and will hesitate to make
reports to authorities for fear of getting into trouble.
According to law-enforcement officials, it is difficult to
get people to testify in court. With hospital personnel,
a query about the day's happenings, meant largely as a
greeting, may get a negative response, as if the person
felt he would be held responsible for anything that might
have gone wrong during the time he was on duty.

Hostility

There is actually a great deal of ridicule, gossip,
slander, and teasing in Virgin Islands society. It is said
that anyone in St. Thomas with a thin skin gets picked
on, and there are many derogatory nicknames based
on some unfortunate physical attribute or incident of
the past. Continentals regard natives as having little
sense of humor. People go to court readily when they
are insulted, and charges of indecent language are com-

mon.[2] The editor of a newspaper in Tortola tells of having run a gossip column in which he included what he considered were strictly innocuous items. A leading citizen objected to the column not because of what had been in it but because of what the writer might say! Senior, writing of the lack of neighborliness among Crucians, has said that their coat of arms should consist of "cross purposes rampant on a field of rumor." Stories of the deliberate spreading of derogatory rumors to obtain someone else's job are common. There are few prominent citizens whose success is not attributed to dishonest dealings or to the rewards of sexual favors. Whether such stories are true or not may be less significant than that they are part of a social pattern and are vehicles for the expressions of feelings of jealousy, fear and hostility. One factor in the situation is that the community is so small that everyone's business gets known and an affront soon becomes public knowledge.

The use of slander and verbal invective is particularly marked in Virgin Islands politics. Speeches in political campaigns commonly contain highly derogatory references to an opponent's private life with no holds barred because of the victim's sex. The history of the islands since the change from naval to civil administration is a record of quarrels with successive governors. The several political parties dispute with one another and among themselves, not in ideological terms nor even so much on matters of policy as on personal grounds. This may be contrasted with the situation in Puerto Rico, where political parties differ fundamentally on the issue of

2. The fact that there are a District Court and two municipal courts for such a small population makes for court cases being heard promptly.

Puerto Rico's relationship to the United States—whether the island should be a commonwealth, a state, or an independent nation.[3]

While there is a great deal of verbally expressed aggression among Virgin Islanders, serious physical violence is relatively uncommon. A march on Government House several years ago that looked menacing to Continentals dissolved harmlessly. The assault and homicide rate is a good deal lower than in the communities in the States of comparable socioeconomic level. Compared with Puerto Ricans, Virgin Islanders seldom use weapons, and fighting and jostling is more common in British Islanders than in natives. Vocal violence is preferred to physical force, and quarrels usually stay in the area of insults and "indecent language." Even in the heat of a fracas, a person may be threatened with a court suit rather than with being physically struck. These points may be illustrated by quoting a popular Calypso dialogue in which the Mighty Sparrow, after abusing and taunting the much larger Lord Melody, finally admonishes him to:

Behave your ugly self, Melody, do what you want but don't get the Sparrow sore, provocation is against the law.

Fears and Superstitions

Along with the avoidance of physical combat there seems, especially in the lower class, to be a feeling of helplessness in a hostile world and a great fear of the vicissitudes of the physical environment. People are very

3. This was true until the recent formation of the Christian Action party as the secular arm of the Roman Catholic Church in Puerto Rico.

afraid of accidents, illness, and death, and danger seems to be ever present. There seems to be a great exaggeration of the hazards of sleeping alone, of exposure to the night air, of being "tiefed,"[4] of going out in the rain,[5] and of finding a centipede in the house. Native Virgin Islanders are generally afraid of the water, and fishing and sailing are done by the French and British West Indians.

The many superstitions that are current in the Virgin Islands have more to do with harm and disaster than with good fortune. While superstitions may not be as universally held as in past years, they remain an important social force. Although educated persons are apt to joke about superstitions and laugh at them, almost everyone can cite some incident that is supposedly explicable only by supernatural agents.

Jarvis has recorded a number of superstitions still prevalent in St. Thomas. They relate mainly to pregnancy and childbirth, illness, and death. A small lizard in the house is considered to be a sign of pregnancy. A pregnant woman may mark a child by seeing ugly things, by holding on to her body when excited, or by having a desire to eat unusual things. A pregnant woman should not cross her legs or the baby will be born in the wrong position. A child's life span is determined by the time it takes its "navel string" to drop to the ground. A caul

4. "Tiefed" is a local term meaning robbed. To me, on the other hand, Virgin Islanders seemed quite honest.

5. Many Virgin Islanders are convinced that one will inevitably catch a cold if exposed to the rain. Others talk of the rain causing germs to sink into the scalp; women are concerned about the damage to a coiffure. A rainy day justifies the postponement of business. In a labor riot in 1892, precipitated by the Mexican silver crisis, Danish troops were about to fire when it rained and everybody went home.

should be burned, or the child will grow up to become a "juvenile delinquent" or have the ability to see ghosts. Widows should wear black underwear to prevent false pregnancy. Two pregnant women should not live together, as the younger will lose her baby.

It is also believed that the constant crying of a child betokens ill tidings and that the child should be whipped into silence with an old shoe. Children should not be allowed to play with their own shadows. It is unlucky to wear purple or black satin, and one should not hold a mirror in a thunderstorm. Birds and crowing roosters may also be harbingers of trouble. It is also said that one should not pay bills on the first of the month. Several persons told Jarvis that a werewolf in Kommandant Gade (street) had so frightened a pregnant Antiguan woman, despite a hortatory cross chalked on the doors of the house, that her husband had to stand by nightly with his cutlass to protect her. Werewolves are believed to be older, hairy, non-Negro men who may suck blood from a pregnant woman even without coming into direct contact with her.

Many of these superstitions involve themes that are important elements in the social patterns of Virgin Islanders. Superstitions are not simply exaggerated or irrational fears, but they serve as modes of adaptation to stress by the way they organize the environment and identify the speaker with significant cultural values. For Virgin Islanders these concern principally children, pregnancy, and death. Like a delusion in a psychosis, the superstition may be a highly condensed, concretized symbol of problems and relationships. For example, the belief about werewolves that was cited may be an expression of a fear of having blood drawn by a doctor and of the widespread opinion, lay and medical, that people in the Virgin Islands are anemic (despite general knowledge that lower blood counts are usual in subtropical areas).

Food as a Symbol

In St. Thomas eating is not important as a medium of social intercourse, while in St. Croix it is a more significant element in social patterns. Lower-class St. Thomian families often do not eat together, and meals are apt to be a casual operation in which each member of the household, even a child, helps himself and eats outside, on the doorstep, or in the living room. In poorer families, one is aware of the smallness of the quarters, the absence of refrigeration in many homes, and the high price of food and utensils in the Virgin Islands. Yet even in wealthier families, eating arrangements tend to be informal. In contrast to a Puerto Rican or French home, a casual visitor is rarely offered something to eat. One minister complained that he had never been able to organize a church supper; and when they are held, some people prefer to take the food home and eat it there. Some confess that they are ashamed of their manners, but this problem would not occur if eating were a part of a social pattern. Crucian families are more likely to eat together, and in St. Croix there is more interest in traditional dishes like *kallilu* and *fungee*.[6] St. Thomians when entertaining at dinner are more likely

6. *Kallilu* is a highly seasoned okra and spinach soup. According to Jarvis, the term also refers to a disturbance or fracas. *Fungee* is corn-meal mush.

to serve some Continental type of food. There is a tendency to deprecate native products, such as tannia and breadfruit, in favor of canned nectars or other relatively expensive, imported products.

Psychotic Reactions

As might be anticipated from the way people structure many of their interpersonal relationships in terms of violence and from their expectations of a hazardous physical environment, there is a high incidence of delusions and hallucinations about assault and killing among native Virgin Islanders (thirty-two of sixty-eight cases) and Tortolans (eight of twenty-two cases).

Patients heard voices threatening to kill them or expressed the belief that they were being harmed in some way. One old man heard a voice saying that one of his children was "bawling" in the yard and that he, himself, would be hung. A woman who felt that she had not been treated with proper respect claimed that the male attendant had beaten her. Such charges seem to stress the indignity rather than the sexual aspects of the offense. Several patients introduced some local touches, one claiming that the members of a steel band were trying to cut him, while another man saw stones being thrown at him. In view of the sensitivity of native Virgin Islanders to gossip and slander, it was of interest that "voices" often called patients bad names and talked about them. One man from St. Croix in the hospital in St. Thomas became disturbed that the "voices" were calling him names. An enquiry revealed that they were calling him a "Crucian."

The following case record indicates the occurrence of

representations of violence in psychotic delusions and confabulations:

CASE REPORT

The patient was a forty-six-year-old Crucian woman whose admission was occasioned by great hostility shown to her nineteen-year-old son with whom she lived. When the police called to escort her to the hospital, she chased them away with a machete. She had worked for a number of years as a domestic in Puerto Rico and had two O.W. children, the boy by a Virgin Islander and a fifteen-year-old girl by a Puerto Rican. She presented a mixed euphoric and paranoid manner and complained that people were talking about her, calling her names, and trying to look into her house. She claimed that five men had come to her house with a gun and shot her in the head. At other times it was one man who had shot her several times. One day during the playing of a record of a famous Negro entertainer, she became agitated, claiming he was the father of her daughter, but she would not marry him because he had treated her badly. For a time she would not take medication from anyone except a janitor with whom she was in love, but then refused for fear his wife would beat her up. She had an episode in which she said that the Lord had given her the power to see the future. As she improved, she talked a great deal about her children, attributing her condition to their staying out at night so that she could not sleep. She felt that they had not been grateful for all she had done for them. Actually, while her daughter was something of a problem, her nineteen-year-old boy was a dutiful and responsible son.

This case shows many features of what might be called a classical Virgin Islands psychosis, with themes of violence, religion, and children. She represents the problem of there being something wrong with her head in the confabulation of having been shot in the head, the multiple shots and the number of men doing the shooting being expressions of the intensity of her fears. Her own hostile feelings and acts seem to be expressed in accounts of the violence of men, an expectation characteristic of many Virgin Islands women. The idea of people looking into her house and talking about her is a familar preoccupation of Virgin Islanders.

While delusions or hallucinations about food occurred in four instances among Crucians, only a single St. Thomian expressed the idea that his food had been poisoned. Similarly, the feeding of St. Thomian patients was not a problem even in disturbed cases.[7] This incidence parallels the degree to which eating is an element in the social patterns in the two islands. In Chapter 10 this will be contrasted with the great importance of eating in the social patterns and psychotic reactions of Puerto Ricans.

In summary, a great deal of status for Virgin Islanders is defined in everyday personal transactions. There is emphasis on proper behavior and dress, and overt signs of respect or derogation. The importance of such tokens may be enhanced by the relative lack of such sources of ascribed status as ethnic group and family. There is a great fear of physical disaster. Hostility is expressed verbally rather than physically, and the symbols in which both fears and hostilities are expressed are structured into social patterns. In psychotic delusions and hallucinations

7. In a follow-up study of Virgin Islands patients sent to St. Elizabeth's in Washington, Miss Schulterbrandt and I found that only the Crucians reacted to the unfamiliarity of the new surrounding by not eating.

themes of violence are frequent. Eating is a more important component of social patterns in St. Croix than in St. Thomas, and delusions about food are much more common in Crucians. This correlation coupled with the data on Puerto Ricans to be presented in Chapter 10 affords one of the best examples of how the content of a delusional system corresponds to the degree to which a symbolic element is used in the significant patterns of social relatedness.

6 LANGUAGE

A DESCRIPTION of everyday Virgin Islands speech in some of its syntactical and semantic aspects is included in line with the thesis that language is a guide to reality. Dialects, colloquialisms, slang, and ungrammatical usages are not simply the speech of uneducated persons but are important indicators of how reality is perceived. Like delusions themselves, such forms of speech are modes of adaptation to stress and as such are pertinent to our study.

Although the Danes ruled their West Indian islands for 250 years, there are practically no Danish remnants in local speech. In St. Thomas this is surprising to a newcomer, who sees the many old Danish buildings, reads such street signs as Regierungs Gade, Prindsessen Gade, and Kommandant Gade and hears names such as Jensen pronounced in Danish fashion. In practice, the streets are rarely called by their proper names, but are referred to as "Main Street" and the "street by the Catholic church," and Anglo-Saxon surnames among the people far outnumber Danish ones. Similarly, no "Africanisms" occur in the ordinary speech of native Virgin Islanders. The people speak a dialect of English known locally as "Calypso." There are no written texts, and standard English is taught in the schools. Despite a considerable effort to eliminate the dialect from pupils' speech as part of the preparation for higher education, it persists in all but a few speakers. There is some difference between the speech of St. Thomas and St. Croix. Each is a variant of a Caribbean "lingua franca" that is mutually intelligible among West Indians and, in varying degrees, unintelligible to outsiders.

The over-all impression one gets of Virgin Islands dialect is of a rapid, rhythmical speech that sounds so different from standard American English, or any other American dialect, that tourists or newcomers often think that the natives are speaking Danish or some exotic West Indian language. Virgin Islanders are vocal rather than verbal, and their speech is repetitive with a rather limited lexicon. The listener is struck by the great range of tone, pitch, and volume in a single sentence. The usual voice quality is low and soft but it rises in pitch and volume, as well as increasing in rapidity, under excitement, which occurs often. There is a tendency to put primary stress on the final syllable, as in the words "hospi*tal*," "Eng*lish*," "tea*cher*," and "ba*by*." Compounds may have changed in stress and in juncture as in "high *school*." No juncture is heard in a phrase like "That's English man" pronounced "Englishman." Conspicuous differences in phonology in-

clude the use of "a" in words like "man," "ma'am," and
steel "band." The sound "aw" in the word "water" is
heard as [wæteh].

Verbs are frequently not inflected for the third person.
People say "he give him" for both "he gives" and "he
gave." There is substitution of the present for the past
tense, such as using "I give" for "I gave" in describing a
past action. Auxiliary verbs such as "am" may be omitted
as in saying "I going home" instead of "I am going home."
The possessive final "s" is apt to be left off as in "my
mother house" instead of "my mother's house." Another
local characteristic is to change the word order as in
"where it is?" for "where is it?"; or a simple substitution
in sequence as "go it over" for "go over it." Nouns may
be used as verbs as in "sexing" or being "advantaged" by
someone. Prepositions are used differently. One is more
apt to work "to" somebody than "for" somebody. A girl
does not have a child by a man but "for" him, a woman
is jealous "after" a man or someone may complain "for"
his head rather than "about" or "of" it. Personal pronoun
cases show wide variation from speaker to speaker and
at different times in the same speaker. Examples are
"him hit I," "we got we gun," "show she" (show her),
and "she gone pregnant for he."[1]

Older and obscure or poetic meanings of words persist.
One's surname is his "title." "Needless" refers to being
needy or in want. "Onliest" is an intensive superlative

1. In discussing the drift away from the old Indo-European system of syntactic cases, Sapir asks if leveling "I" and "me" to a
single case would not be to un-English our language beyond recognition. He adds that (fortunately) there is no drift toward such
horrors as "me see him" or "I see he" (P. 166). Such "horrors" are
very much a part of Virgin Islands dialect.

form of "only." To "dismiss" is used in the sense of to break up or separate. To "reach" is used for "arrive," so one may be asked what time he "reached." Also, Virgin Islanders, like Virginians, do not go to a doctor, but are "carried" and a doctor doesn't treat a patient but "has him in charge." The months of the year and days of the week may be designated as "May month" and "Saturday day." "Mistress" for "Mrs." is still used. To "pimp" is to tell tales about someone, or to peep or eavesdrop. To "pass by" may be used in its obsolete sense of going through or traveling through a place and may refer to a visit of any length. Thus, one girl told how she had become pregnant on the occasion of a young man "passing by." Another woman, who had become pregnant during her hospital stay, commented that she had been "gifted" with a baby. One may not refer to an ancestor as a Dane but as a "Dane man." People may be not so much upset and annoyed as "harrassed" or "vexed" and, when severely so, "humbugged." "Frightful" is used in its more archaic meaning of "fearful" such as a "fearful child." Many forms of mistreatment come under the head of being "brutalized."

It is significant that in stressful situations a person may speak quite correct English except when he comes to describe some exciting or disturbing incident, at which point he will lapse into colloquial speech. For example, a witness giving testimony in court began his account of the activities of the accused with formal references to "Your Honor" and how the "party of the first part did proceed," and so forth. When he reached the climax of the story, he lapsed into colloquial speech with, "Then, man, he mash up (the house)."

The interjection "man," pronounced "mon" to rhyme

with "con" in Scottish fashion, is an important token in the definition of interpersonal relationships. It is both a form of address and an ejaculation denoting emphasis and a particularly fervent or confidential note as in, "Why no, man, you can't do that!" It is used among adults, men and women, by adults to children, among children, and even by a person to a goat or a chicken, but not by children to adults. A Continental who had lived in St. Thomas for several months exultingly exclaimed that he felt he really belonged when a native addressed him as "man." The term seems to have the same significance as the French *tu* or the German *du* in bringing the speaker into an emotional relationship with the listener and imparting a special feeling of intimacy to the verbal form. It may be compared to "man" as an ejaculation in stateside English, but there it is used exclusively among men. One wonders if the difference reflects the greater equality of the sexes in Virgin Islands society while preserving the differentiation of children from adults.

Another feature of Virgin Islands speech is the distinctive way in which the physical self is designated. Where a Continental would say he was going to "wash himself," a Virgin Islander "washes his skin." A Virgin Islander "rests his body," but avoids getting his "neck choked." One is more apt to "get a fist" than be punched. An account of an experience in which the speaker thought he was seeing spirits was climaxed by his making his escape by "jumping his body on a horse." Actually, a remark about washing one's "self" may bring snickers, since in local speech the term also refers to the genital region. In listening to accounts of quarrels, I often heard how someone's fist happened to have gotten on to someone else's face, or how a hand happened to be attached to a stick, which was in contact with another person's body. One might speculate as to the significance of thus seeming to give independent existence to the several parts of the body. It may be germane to Virgin Islanders' emphasis on the physical self as opposed to the social self. Thus, in the great emphasis on personal cleanliness and proper dress to the comparative neglect of the home and the streets, it seems as if the "self" does not extend beyond the skin and its coverings.[2] Such a way of referring to one's self may also be related to Virgin Islanders' great fears about bodily injury and illness. This may be contrasted with an attitude in which the integrity of the self transcends physical considerations and bodily discomforts.

The fearful, fate-propitiating attitudes of native Virgin Islanders toward illness are shown in the ordinary social amenities and everyday forms of greeting. When a Virgin Islander is asked how he is feeling, he rarely replies that he feels fine or that he is, "very well, thank you." Rather, he is "not too bad," or he is "nothing worse," or "betwixt and between," or, especially if he has been ill, he may go as far as to say that he is "plenty better."[3] This may reflect not only the great fear of illness but the almost complete absence of verbal denial of illness in Virgin

2. Campbell in his study of St. Thomas in 1943 emphasized the lack of community mindedness and the lack of social groups other than the church. He attributed this to the egocentricity of St. Thomians, which was in turn derived from the insecure family background and laissez-faire economic conditions. While the interpretation may be questioned, the observations indicate the way the social self is defined.

3. M. G. Lewis, visiting his Jamaica estates in 1816, comments that "quite so so" means "a great deal better" in Negro dialect.

Islands society. In a similar situation a Continental would usually respond to such a greeting with a remark such as, "fine, thank you" even though he may be having a hang-over and feeling anything but fine. He would regard it as impolite or out of place to indicate his actual clinical condition, and this reflects a common, deeper attitude that the maintenance of health is tied up with responsibility and self-respect. Such dyadic interchanges produce a social self that is somehow quite independent of any physical ailment that may exist. The question arises as to whether the persistence of such expressions as being "carried" to a doctor and being in "charge" may not reflect feelings of helplessness in the face of illness.

The expressions that a woman "makes a baby" or is pregnant "for" a man accurately reflect the reality of the social situation in terms of the relationships between the sexes in Virgin Islands culture. This usage may be contrasted to that of stateside English and other languages in which a woman has a baby "by" or "from" or "of" a man. To say that a woman makes a baby "for" a man implies that she has done the job largely on her own and of her own free choice. The social role of the woman as the main producer of the child is seen in another expression quoted from a letter to my wife from a youngster complaining of her father's neglect:

He doesn't study on having any daughter named Ivy. He is just supporting an old island woman who he got a girl child by last year.

In conclusion, it may be asked if such forms of language predetermine as well as represent attitudes and practises concerning health and illness, pregnancy and parenthood, and bodily injury and "defilement." Certainly, people persist in so speaking and feel that they express themselves more meaningfully even though correct grammar is in a sense known and more standard English is used in other contexts. Yet, in this feeling they are unaware of the larger social reality to which they are subscribing. It may be that language expresses identity through the very social patterns that it helps to perpetuate.

7 RELIGION AND SYMBOLIC ASPECTS OF DEATH

Religion

RELIGIOUS TERMS and symbols pervade Virgin Islands life. Particularly in persons of Tortolan origin, they provide a framework for structuring the environment and expressing feelings. Along with roles derived from the parent-child relationship, religion is the most important source of identity in Virgin Islands society. Father Levo, an Anglican priest who lived for many years in the British and American Virgin Islands, commented that when events were depicted in religious language, they gained an immediate, personal, and readily grasped quality. Thus, feelings about slavery would become particularly poignant when put in terms of the bondage of the children of Israel.

Religious teaching in the Protestant churches is con-

135

servative and based on belief in the Bible and faith in
Jesus in a personal sense. It is authoritarian, and there
is a great deal of respect for and deference to ministers,
who, except in the Methodist Church, are white Continentals. Membership in different churches is not a divi-
sive factor, and family members may belong to different
sects without any apparent conflict. In some homes, the
children may each go to a different church. The churches
attempt to set up proper standards of behavior for their
congregations, and in earlier days lists of approved forms
of conduct were actually posted. Ministers and congregations condemn illegitimacy, though in most instances
sacraments are not refused to O.W. mothers as they are
in the British islands.

Religious observations are important sources of identity.
Membership in the few small "outside" churches is limited,
and most Virgin Islanders regard them as lacking in
dignity, even though these sects do not have emotional
displays as extreme as those found in the American South.
The established churches themselves are old buildings
with considerable architectural charm. A good deal of
tradition is associated with them, the Anglican church,
for instance, having been built by the congregation itself,
free and slave, in the 1830's. As has been said, the churches
historically have filled important needs for Virgin Islanders. For a person from a loosely structured family with
few sources of identity and status, religion imparts a
particularly vivid meaning and substance to events and
relationships. For the bulk of Virgin Islanders, not only
the more devout ones, interpersonal relationships are
divided into those virtuous aspects that are God's will and
those sinful actions that are the work of the Devil. Proper

dress, polite speech, and honest work acquire divine
sanction; and even acts that are contrary to church tenets
are still thought of in religious terms. People living in
"sin" may still go to church but refrain from taking
communion.

Considerable prestige is associated with church activities. People like to have a new house blessed by a minister.
All children are baptized. While parents are eager to
have children confirmed, church attendance is often lax
once this goal is achieved. People desire the status of a
communicant, though some ministers feel that they value
the prestige more than the experience of the communion.
Virgin Islanders generally are not preoccupied with
doubts of personal worthiness and questions of whether
they will attain salvation. Rather, those who are "saved"
consider it as an achievement and often as an opportunity
to be "one up" on those less favored.

The language of religion is used freely in everyday life.
Not only are arguments involving moral issues put in
religious terms, but "please God" or "if God spare me"
is commonly appended to statements about the future. It
is as if the words give to the expectation a particular
quality of truth or destiny. Workmen on a job may sing
hymns. For some people, particularly British Islanders,
reading may be confined to the Bible and religious tracts.
Letters regularly contain religious sentiments. Tortola
is actually known as the "Holy Island." There is a very
popular religious disk-jockey program from Vieques,
Puerto Rico, in which congratulatory messages and birthday greetings are conveyed through the playing of favorite
hymns. The large number of religious holidays has been
mentioned. Religious pictures are common in homes and

may be the only art displayed. (However, sometimes facing a calendar with a highly colored representation of Jesus there may be another with a picture of a seductively clad "cover girl.")

In stressful situations, people who are otherwise inarticulate can express themselves in religious terms. I recall a frightened ten-year-old child in a psychiatric interview, whom I attempted to put at ease with an opening remark, "Who made your pretty braids?" She replied, "God." An eight-year-old boy from one of the British islands would not answer to any of the usual gambits as to where he lived or went to school, but when asked to give the Ten Commandments, he began promptly with, "Thou shalt not covet thy neighbor's house. Thou shalt not covet thy neighbor's wife, nor . . ." Then there was the case of the woman who, in a recent disastrous flood in St. Thomas, seemed paralyzed with fear but was heartened and mobilized into effective action by her daughter's assurance that the Bible said the world would be destroyed by fire, not water. Religious references also provide the content for such verbal security operations as explanations, complaints, justifications, and rationalizations. Many people feel that the flood was God's punishment for the sinful wickedness of Carnival. One woman justified the theft of some mangoes growing on church property by asserting that the tree had been planted by God.[1]

1. Henriques, writing of Jamaican society, believes that people find justification for even O.W. pregnancy in Biblical teaching. He cites the story of Sarah and Hagar, noting the scorn expressed for the barren Sarah, the generosity with which she permits Abraham to take Hagar, and how with the status gained from conceiving a child at the age of ninety-one, she drives Hagar and her child into the wilderness.

Symbolic Aspects of Death

The representation of death is an important symbol for
Virgin Islanders, especially those from the island of Tortola. It figures not only in the great fear of death but in
ceremonial activities such as funerals, in religious beliefs, in ideas about the supernatural, and in superstitions.

Funerals in the Virgin Islands are highly ritualized
community events. In St. Thomas, there are no professional undertakers, and the funeral involves an announcement of the death on the radio accompanied by a dirge
and a procession through town by many mourners dressed
in black, or white, or lavender. As the procession goes
by, pedestrians are expected to go indoors and close their
doors. People who have been away from the islands for
years will return for a funeral. There may be a great deal
of discussion in a congregation as to what type of a
funeral the deceased is entitled, whereas in the States
such a matter would be determined by how elaborate a
ceremony the family wished to pay for.

In Tortola, funerals are of even greater importance,
exceeding in both elaborateness of ritual and emotional
significance the ceremonies associated with birth and
marriage. Funerals are among the very few social functions of Tortolan life, and one attends a funeral even
without knowing the deceased. There is an exact formula
as to the route to be taken by the funeral procession,
and long discussions are held about it. The head must
always be pointed toward the west and if a short cut
is inadvertently taken, it means that someone in the
family will be "cut off."

Virgin Islanders, especially those from the British islands, are greately concerned with the activities of the spirits of the deceased. In Tortola it is believed that everyone has two spirits. After death, the good spirit goes to Jesus while the evil spirit stays in the grave. For nine days it can be harmful and has to be placated by mourners versed in the necessary ceremonies. The grave spirit can cause disease, bring about abortion, and precipitate sudden death. Spirits can be awakened from the grave, but they must be paid, the money going to the watchman of the cemetery, who puts it into the grave. There is a second set of spirits that are less harmful and have to do with aphrodisiacs and philters. A third type concerns crops and plantings.

Tortolans believe actively in spirits, or "jumbies" as they are known, and measures are taken against their activities. These consist in keeping a bottle of turpentine in the house, in marking a cross on the door, and in speaking to the jumby very roughly. It is believed that jumbies hide behind cactus, so that throwing sand in that direction is advisable. Mushrooms and other fungi are thought to be produced by jumbies, hence the names "jumby fish pot" and "jumby umbrella.'" Also it is helpful to keep a "frizzy" fowl about the house to dig up buried charms, and good to put a child's first tooth into a spider hole. One should not open letters if one doesn't know the handwriting, and even then only on certain days. With an unfamiliar writing, the four corners of the envelope should first be burned. Some persons have a great fear of being pallbearers, and dirt from a graveyard has special qualities.

In states of anxiety and depression, feelings of guilt,

fear, and isolation are readily structured in terms of religions and death.

CASE REPORT

Mrs. J, a thirty-three-year-old seamstress came to the psychiatric clinic complaining that "I'm just living in fear as if I am going to die. My heart used to beat plenty and frighten me as if I were going to die. I'll start blaspheming and cussing and get a fear that God will punish me and I will die." She described dreams about death and graveyards and fears of going crazy.

Her symptoms had begun three weeks previously with a feeling that she must say a bad word about God. She had sought advice from friends who told her to pray, and had gone to physicians who treated her for "pus on the kidney" and "pressure." She recalled that she had begun to "feel funny" after two women of her acquaintance had developed cancer.

The patient had been born in St. Thomas and said she had left school at the age of fifteen to work after her mother had died of a heart attack. She had five children, four of them out of wedlock and the youngest "for" her present husband. Though they had lived together for ten years and had saved enough money to purchase a home, the couple had been married only three years and then at the insistence of the Catholic priest. The patient had been born a Catholic but was attending one of the smaller Protestant churches, because, she claimed, "The Catholics don't leave you read the Bible. They ain't teaching you according to the Bible." Her husband was an Anglican, who said he had married her in the Catholic church so that she would not be excommunicated.

The husband described the patient as a hard-working, worrisome person, conscientious about her obligations. He told of how, if she had promised someone to finish a job, she would stay up until two or three o'clock. She worried about the children, about their using bad words, or if some other parent criticized them. "If a child got a poor report card, she might punish him by not letting him go to the movies but then forget to punish him because she loved him so much." Mr. J said he used to drink, but had stopped. He thought her first companion had treated her quite badly and he had felt sorry for her.

The patient was hospitalized, at first protesting that she could not leave her children. After several days she showed clinical improvement in that she expressed only an occasional idea of death and punishment by God. These were replaced by many somatic complaints of palpitation, constipation, belching, and a pressure about her eyes. After several therapeutic interviews, she talked of her problems in interpersonal terms. She told of her difficulties with her neighbors, who made her nervous, and her fear that the other patients might harm her. She also expressed disapproval of her husband and felt that her troubles came from worrying about him, and recalled that her first companion had satisfied her more sexually. She thought she might take her children and visit her sisters in the States. The patient was discharged after twenty days of hospitalization with marked improvement, which she has maintained.

Psychotic Reactions

Delusions and hallucinations concerning religion were especially prominent in British Virgin Islands patients, occurring in ten of the twenty-two patients in the group. They were less frequent among natives, appearing in twelve of the sixty-eight patients. The majority of these delusions and hallucinations concerned God and Jesus. A woman from St. Croix heard a voice telling her that she would sit on the right hand of God in Bethlehem. A patient from St. John refused to leave her room in the hospital because she was busy with God's work, which seemed to consist of making long lists of various objects. One patient claimed that he was Jesus Christ, while another said he was the son of Jesus. A girl talked about burning in hell for her sins. In excited states there was a great deal of praying and quoting from the Bible. Sometimes prayer and profanity were combined as in the instance of a woman who "praised God for giving me the strength to bust his damn ass in." In several cases, the onset of the psychosis was marked by great religious activity. One woman insisted on having her children kneel down and pray all day. (It is likely that if her children had not been involved, she would not have been hospitalized.) Patients described a great deal of obsessive thinking about God and Jesus and feelings of fear, anger, guilt, and shame were often presented in religious language.

Delusions and hallucinations about death were also most common among British Virgin Islanders (eight out of twenty-two cases). In native Virgin Islanders the incidence was ten out of sixty-eight. The majority of the ideas about death also involved religion and the spirit world. Patients said, for example, that they had talked with the spirits of dead persons or reported having seen dead relatives. Several patients stated that they were dead as a result of punishment by God. A woman claimed that spirits had put a dead boy in her. Another saw a dead child in a well and heard the screams of dying children. A man from St. Thomas would misidentify me variously by the names of doctors who had died in St. Thomas, one of whom, he claimed, was my "spiritual self."

A characteristic psychotic reaction, featuring themes of religion, death, children, and masculine violence, was seen in young women, particularly in the Tortolan group. In one hallucination a woman saw a man standing over her with a knife and heard a voice saying "bye, bye baby." The onset was acute and symptoms of no more than one or two weeks' duration were usually reported. In seven of thirteen such cases, the patient had become ill within several months of having had a baby. On admission to the hospital, the patients were in a state of catatonic excitement or were mute and stuporous. Some relatives attributed the condition to obeah, the husband of one patient stating that she had been bewitched by a cat.

In the early stages patients were incontinent of urine but this did not persist. Patients were frequently aggressive to male hospital personnel. They also made sexual gestures, though these were not accompanied by delusions about sex. The psychotic period rarely lasted more than two or three weeks, and with clinical improvement somatic symptoms commonly appeared. Also, patients who were married became quite hostile to their husbands as in refusing to talk to them and, in several instances a relapse occurred after a trial visit home.

In summary, the Church is probably the most important institution in Virgin Islands society, and religious beliefs and language provide a significant source of identity. Such symbols furnish a scheme for organizing the events of the environment, serving as a means of structuring and expressing feelings and as a yardstick for ethical concepts. The symbolic representation of death in funeral customs, in superstitions and in ideas that the spirits of the dead can return to harm the living are likewise an important social force, especially among Virgin Islanders from the British islands. In psychotic reactions, there is a relatively high incidence of delusions and hallucinations about religion and death.

8   OBEAH, OR WITCHCRAFT

BELIEF IN, and the practice of, obeah, as witchcraft is known in the West Indies, still prevails among British Virgin Islanders, French, and Puerto Ricans and to some extent among native Virgin Islanders. While obeah is more widespread in Tortola than in the American islands, it is still of significance as a social force in St. Croix, St. John, and St. Thomas. In this chapter, obeah will be considered first as a social pattern and secondly as a therapeutic process.

In the Virgin Islands obeah is not a formal institution. It does not have a priesthood or a system of initiation into its mysteries. Nor is there a pantheon as in Haitian voodoo. Practitioners exist, but they are not revered as the wise men of the community. They operate in surreptitious fashion, and it is difficult to seek them out. Obeah is forbidden by law, and the belief that a charm will not work if the obeah man is arrested adds to the secrecy. The occupation is a part-time one, carried on by both men and women, who are usually from the British or French islands. The reputation of a practitioner seems to vary with the distance of his regular provenience from the Virgin Islands, those from Guadeloupe and Martinique being credited with the most awesome feats. They are reputed as being able to cause and cure illness, kill people by magical means, drive them crazy, and counter the spells of other obeah men.

Obeah as a Social Pattern

The degree of belief in obeah is extremely difficult to evaluate and the significance of obeah goes far beyond a matter of belief or disbelief in any absolute sense. Actually, obeah seems to be believed in some contexts and not in others. While a person may charge that his illness has been caused by obeah, he usually consults a physician. Even among educated people who express disbelief, obeah figures in social patterns. Talking about obeah is a means of jesting and teasing, and people frighten others and play "practical jokes" by "planting" some article, such as a coin used in the art. A woman may reassure herself as to the faithfulness of a spouse by some gesture of obeah or console herself over the defection of a lover by attributing a rival's success to the work of an obeah woman. Yet her friends may scoff at this explanation. In a similar fashion, Virgin Islanders would no longer take seriously a businessman who attributed his failure to a competitor having "put something" on him. However, just as someone might avoid walking under a ladder, a Virgin Islander might hesitate to pick up a coin off the street lest it be "fixed."

There seems often to be no incompatibility between religion and obeah. Religious faith, belief in obeah, and superstitious fear are intermingled. Parents have their children baptized to protect them against spirits. A woman in St. Thomas regularly took the sacraments of the Catholic Church as a precaution against obeah. Another commonly used method of prophylaxis is to mark crosses on the palms and soles before retiring at night. The literature on obeah in the West Indies cites many other examples. Father J. J. Williams, a Catholic priest, commented that Jamaican Negroes regarded the Roman Catholic Church as exercising the strongest obeah. He also thought the great desire for baptism was an effort to obtain a weapon against obeah. Sereno noted in the residence of an obeah man in Dominica a little altar replete with images of the saints and a burning taper. Raymond Smith states that "belief in obeah and spirit possession may exist in a framework of Old Testament morality."

Some authors believe that obeah is a survival of African customs. Yet Europeans and Americans believed in witchcraft well into the eighteenth century, and belief in spirits was strong in Scotland and England, whence most of the planters came. The use of hair combings and of apparel soaked in the prospective victim's sweat and other body excreta, which prevailed in Europe, does not seem to differ from current practices in the Virgin Islands. Some practitioners seem to have acquired their information from books of occult lore published in the United States. Obeah was widely practised among the slaves, yet the French in the Virgin Islands, who have no history of slavery, are great believers in obeah. In the American rural South, slaves of the same provenience as West Indian Negroes developed superstitious practices like those of their white neighbors.

Regardless of historical origin, obeah persists because it serves as a mode of adaptation to stress, because it structures and expresses the most intense feelings and organizes what would otherwise be uncontrollable and unpredictable forces. While much of the apparatus may have been brought from Africa, obeah was a vital institution of slavery because it furnished a social matrix and a source of identity for an otherwise rootless people. The emphasis placed on African origins for obeah, both by the plantocracy and the slaves, seems to have been a means of attaining identity.[1]

The following account of obeah in late eighteenth-century Jamaica by Bryan Edwards shows the way in which slave society was organized and regulated by the institution of obeah:

The professors of Obeah are, and always were, natives of Africa, and none other; and they have brought the science with them from thence to Jamaica, where it is so universally practised, that we believe there are few of the large estates possessing native Africans, which have not one or more of them. The oldest and most crafty are those who usually attract the greatest devotion and confidence; those whose hoary heads, and a somewhat peculiarly harsh and forbidding in their aspect, together with a skill in plants of the medicinal and poisonous species, have qualified them for the exercise of this art. The negroes in general, whether Africans or Creoles, revere, consult, and fear them; to these oracles they

1. Renzo Sereno believes that obeah in the Leeward and Windward Islands is most prevalent, and that obeah men have the most prestige in islands like Montserrat and Tortola, in which the decline of agriculture has been associated with social disorganization.

resort, and with the most implicit faith, upon all occasions, whether for the cure of disorders, the obtaining revenge for injuries or insults, the conciliating of favour, the discovery and punishment of the thief or the adulterer, and the prediction of future events. Their incantations, to which the midnight hours are allotted, are studiously veiled in mystery; and as the negroes thoroughly believe in their supernatural power, the stoutest among them tremble at the very sight of the ragged bundle, the bottle, or the egg-shells, which are stuck in the thatch, or hung over the door of a hut, or upon the branch of a plantain tree, to deter marauders. With minds so firmly prepossessed, they no sooner find Obeah set for them near the door of their house, or in the path which leads to it, than they give themselves up for lost. When a negro is robbed of a fowl or a hog, he applies directly to the Obeah man or woman; it is then made known among his fellow blacks, that Obeah is set for the thief; and as soon as the latter hears the dreadful news, his terrified imagination begins to work; no resource is left but in the superior skill of some more eminent Obeahman of the neighbourhood who may counteract the magical operations of the other; but if no one can be found of higher rank and ability, or if after gaining such an ally he should still fancy himself affected, he presently falls into a decline, under the incessant horror of impending calamities. The slightest painful sensation in the head, the bowels, or any other part, any casual loss or hurt, confirms his apprehensions, and he believes himself the devoted victim of an invisible and irresistible agency. Sleep, appetite, and cheerfulness forsake him, his strength decays, his disturbed imagination is haunted without respite, his features wear the settled gloom of despondency: dirt, or any other unwholesome substance, becomes his only food, he contracts a morbid habit of body, and gradually sinks into the grave. A negro, who is taken ill, enquires of the Obeahman the cause of his sickness, whether it will prove mortal or not, and within what time he shall die or recover. The oracle generally ascribes the distemper to the malice of some particular person by name, and advises to set Obeah for that person; but if no hopes are given of recovery, immediate despair takes place, which no medicine can remove, and death is the certain consequence. These anomalous symptoms are found to baffle the skill of the ablest physician. (Pp. 392-394)

One suspects that some of the emphasis on African origin by the planters may have been a denial of their own participation in the system and an excuse for not providing adequate medical care. For example, it was common for planters to have their gardens "dressed" by an obeah man to protect against depredations. Possibly the most important form of recognition of obeah lies in the extremely strict laws, still in force, against the practice of obeah and the possession of instruments of the art. An act passed in 1904 by the legislature of the Leeward Islands made a person guilty if he could not prove that such articles were for other uses.

It is significant that leaders of slave revolts in the West Indies were often obeah men and that the feelings of courage and invincibility that mobilized the rebels were structured in symbols of obeah. One cannot explain this simply by saying that the drum beating, snake brandishing, and other parts of the ceremony roused primitive African instincts or released suppressed hostilities. These feelings take shape and are perceived as such in large part by reason of the place of the elements of obeah in a pattern of social relatedness.

Today, while obeah is prohibited by law[2] and denounced by the Church, it persists because it is part of a social pattern. It will remain until it is superseded by

2. Writing of the legal aspects of obeah, J. S. Udal, a judge in the Leeward Islands, points out that the law punishes what it says does not exist.

other cultural values and until fears and hostilities gain other channels for expression.[3] While education will be a factor in its disappearance, it will not accomplish this by disproving the existence of the claims of obeah. Rather, education will be part of a cultural broadening in which other symbolic patterns will be used as modes of adaptation to stress. Another point is that in a sense obeah "works." A woman consulting an obeah man about a faithless lover obtained a charm that would make the car he drove go over a cliff. His employer, hearing of it, promptly fired him from his job as a chauffeur.

Obeah as Therapy

It is not uncommon for mentally ill patients to have been first taken to an obeah man. Something of the therapeutic procedure may be learned from the following incident:

CASE REPORT

A twenty-two-year-old Tortolan woman, one week after the delivery of a child, became hyperactive and over-talkative. She repeated the names of numerous dead persons over and over again, and claimed that she had seen their spirits. Her father described her as always having been a quiet and obedient child. "You wouldn't

3. One indication of such a change is the growing practice of defacement of cars in St. Thomas. While a woman might have formerly consulted an obeah man about an errant lover, she can now slash his tires and dent his fenders. While the yearly purchase and possession of automobiles in the Virgin Islands may not yet have become the sanctified ritual that it is in the States, anyone who has watched a Virgin Islander spend a morning polishing a car can appreciate what a significant symbol it has become.

know she was alive." He attributed her condition to either the milk or blood going to her head, or to someone having put a spell on her. He believed that the spell had been placed so that she couldn't move into a new house that her husband was building, and regarded her reciting of the names of the deceased as evidence that the spirits were at work. The spirits could not work on the girl while she was pregnant because they couldn't affect two lives, so they had to wait until the baby was born.

The obeah man began the interview by asking her how she was feeling, whether anyone had hurt her, if she had seen anything unusual and if she had had any "speaks" (quarrels) with neighbors. When she admitted to some quarreling, he "drew out" the "person." The informant said that if it had been necessary to kill the person, the procedure would be to get a Bible and lay open scissors across it. The scissors would then be stuck into the wall, where the offending person's picture would be drawn. If the patient then ran fast enough, she could see the person's body taken to be buried. The therapy also involved "barking" with nine dollars worth of a mixture of cinnamon oil, asafetida, dragon's blood, almond oil, alna oil, Florida water, and white lavender.

While treatment in this case was unsuccessful, the therapeutic significance of as powerful a social force as obeah cannot be dismissed. As has been mentioned, the problem is one of gathering data so that neither a full description of the procedures used or the results obtained is available. Most of my data came from informants who had known "someone" who had gone to an obeah man. Some of the problems for which consultations were made seemed to be simple ones and the therapeutic method relatively uncomplicated. Clients sought advice about picking a winner in a horse race, ensuring the affections of a spouse, or influencing the decision of a magistrate in a court case. They received such instructions as pointing a fish head in the proper direction and holding a particular article in the mouth while in court.

Some people who visit obeah practitioners because they do not feel well are severely disturbed, and their problems and motives are less evident. Here the person and his family are questioned about problems and incidents—has he built a new house recently, has he gotten a new job, or has he had a quarrel? The obeah man then usually decides that the illness has been caused by the malicious act of an envious person, perhaps abetted by another practitioner. As in the case described, the obeah man then performs the appropriate ceremony, such as laying open scissors across a Bible and often making some reference to the malign actions of spirits. This "spirit" may be drawn out by a magnet. Another factor that may be of considerable therapeutic importance is that the procedure is very expensive.

How obeah works, and indeed it may, is of course as complex a question to consider as is the understanding of any form of psychotherapy. It is not simply a matter of suggestion or the credibility of unsophisticated people. Nor can it be adequately explained on the basis of an abreaction and a "release of repressed hostility." While suggestions are made and hostility is evoked, they function as therapeutic processes because they are put into language of such socially significant content. Symbols of religion, violence, and death particularly, subserve the most intense emotional relationships for Virgin Islanders and structure the events of the environment into organized wholes. When the obeah man says that a neighbor is envious or covetous and that hostility exists, he is generally not far from the truth. When such a relationship is put into the metaphors and the rest of the symbolic apparatus of obeah, then it gains an overwhelmingly vivid quality of meaning and reality. In effect, a delusional system is created. The therapeutic mechanism does not seem to be fundamentally different from that of spontaneously occurring psychoses in which delusions and hallucinations about obeah, religion, and death appear. In each case these symbols are used in attempts to organize the environment and establish identity.

Psychotic Reactions

In patients hospitalized for psychotic reactions, delusions and hallucinations about obeah occurred most frequently among British Virgin Islanders (seven of twenty-two cases), French (five of sixteen cases), and Puerto Ricans (six of twenty-two cases) and less commonly among native Virgin Islanders (six of sixty-eight cases). One interesting example of a delusion about obeah occurred in a woman who thought her husband had been changed into a werewolf by an obeah man because he was "looking well vexed and puffed up." In another case, a woman had psychotic episodes after several pregnancies in which she had delusions about children. Her husband, a British Islander, blamed all the difficulties of the family on "brutal ill-treatment by the government." This had grown out of an incident in which a child had wandered off and had been found in a neglected condition at another farm. He claimed that the police had accused him of cutting the child in half, burying one part under the bed, and feeding the other to the hogs. Also, he stated that the child's body had been "corrupted" and had to be taken to another island for a cure involving some sort of magic.

In many families of psychotic patients, the relatives held the same basic ideas about obeah as the patient and attributed the illness to the workings of witchcraft. The following case abstract illustrates how delusions of obeah not only appear as condensed symbols of the patient's problems and relationships, but express the motives of other members of the family as well.

CASE REPORT

A twenty-six-year-old woman, a native of St. John, was admitted to the hospital in a state of agitation. The onset had been an acute one of one week's duration. She talked of having seen the spirit of a man and having heard voices saying that she would die, because a spell had been put upon her. She also stated that "things" were crawling on her. After three weeks of hospitalization she was discharged as improved only to have a recurrence, also of brief duration.

The patient was the mother of five children, the youngest of whom was six-months old at the time of admission. She had been married for a year, but lived with her mother while her husband lived with his mother in the same yard. The patient had wanted to live with her husband but this had been discouraged by her mother, who stated that another woman with whom the husband had been friendly would put obeah on her. The husband dated the onset of the patient's illness from the time he had come home after a visit to his "outside wife." He believed that the "outside wife" had put an evil spirit on his wife. During the acute illness the sight of her husband seemed to produce an exacerbation in the patient.

In summary, belief in obeah is still current in the Virgin Islands, particularly among Tortolans, French, and Puerto Ricans. It is a significant element in patterns of social relatedness, and delusions and hallucinations about obeah are prominent in psychotic reactions.

9 THE FRENCH

THE FRENCH, numbering about 1,500 persons, are distinct from native Virgin Islanders not only in color but to a considerable extent in occupation, family organization, social roles, and symbolic values. Through language, ethnic origin, close family connections, and customs, they have maintained considerable identity as Frenchmen. They speak a patois that resembles standard French more than the Creole of Martinique, and when they speak Calypso English, it has a unique French accent. Older people may still not speak English, and they, with the help of traditional customs and costumes, preserve a distinctly French flavor. For instance, Bastille Day is still celebrated annually. While the French community is still a fairly isolated one, their society is changing nevertheless, and within a few years such customs and habits as they retain may disappear.

The French make their living largely as fishermen and sailors, farmers and gardeners. Some engage in inter-island trade, particularly with their home island of St. Barthélemy. Through their ownership of once nearly worthless land, their prosperity has risen in the land boom of recent years. The French are regarded widely as thrifty and hardworking. In the early years of the migration from St. Barthélemy to St. Thomas, they lived in poverty and had a high rate of tuberculosis and diseases stemming from malnutrition. Some now work in the hotels, and the younger women are beginning to work in the stores catering to tourists. They are still not employed in positions on a higher educational level and in government jobs to any extent, nor are they active in the political life of the island.

The French are still clannish, though this is lessening and they are beginning, with the encouragement of the Catholic Church, to intermarry with the natives and Puerto Ricans. They are much less "class conscious" among themselves than are native Virgin Islanders. They have been traditionally very aware of color, using the term "Negro" in referring to the natives. The mountain French, as distinguished from those who live along the water-front, form a community with a leader who plays a paternalistic role, renting land for tiny, superficiary houses for a few cents a month, helping to support widows and generally serving as an intermediary between Continentals and natives. While he was born in Guadeloupe and is quite dark, he is not regarded as a Negro. The French are quite conscious of origins. There is a local tradition that they are descended from escapees from the penal colony of Cayenne, originally sent there for political offenses but coming from good families in France. Mental illness is attributed to hereditary causes and is said to run in certain families.

Family Organization

Family organization differs considerably from that of lower-class Virgin Islanders. French households are based on marriage, and the father is the only, or main, breadwinner and the head of the family. The housework and care of the children are wholly taken over by the mother. Although the French wife has traditionally supplemented the family income by straw work, making mats, hats, and baskets, she is not likely to be employed outside of the home. In actual practice, many households seem to be run by the mother or grandmother, but outward deference is paid to the man, even though he may spend little time in the home. Older people are esteemed and have considerable authority. When widowed, they usually live with or close to their children. In past years a widow wore mourning for the rest of her life, even covering her gold earrings with black.

The mother of a girl exerts a good deal of control even after the girl is married and has her own home. The French marry early, families preferring that daughters do so in order of age. Parents have influence in the choice of a spouse and not infrequently grooms are imported from St. Barthélemy. It is understood that a couple does not marry until the man has a house, and the engagement is not even announced until the house is ready for occupancy. It is usually built on family-owned or leased

land with the help of relatives and friends, and the fact
that a father will give land to a son emphasizes the patriarchal system. The marriage ceremony, beginning with
a service in the Catholic Church, is one of the few occasions for lavish entertaining in the otherwise rather
austere lives of the French.

The French may have liaisons with natives but these
are disapproved. An O.W. child in the home, especially
if colored, is often neglected and mistreated. O.W. pregnancies usually lead to marriage, and O.W. births are not
common. The French feel that they are a disgrace; and if
the man does not offer marriage, the male members of
the girl's family may threaten violent action. Daughters
are strictly chaperoned and are not permitted out at night
even to church-sponsored affairs. Even engaged couples
are given little freedom. In former years, and occasionally
today, one could see a French girl walking on the street
followed a few paces back by a watchful mother. The
French are quite prudish about sex and very modest,
for example, about letting children run about without
clothes. In the frequent family quarrels that go on among
them, the women often accuse one another of marital
infidelity and prostitution. In St. Thomas the nearest
thing to a red-light district is the waterfront Carenage
area, known as Frenchtown or French Village. Entertain-
ment centers about the Normandie Bar, which is "For
Men Only," one of the very few segregated institutions
in the Virgin Islands. There is no organized prostitution
in the Virgin Islands, and the few women making a living
in this way are more apt to be Puerto Rican, or occasionally French, than native.[1]

1. Kingsley Davis states that prostitution exists where there is

Some of the attitudes of the French concerning parenthood, sex, and color are shown in the following case:

CASE REPORT

A twenty-one-year-old French laborer came to the clinic
complaining of nervousness and palpitation. He said
he had been drinking heavily over the past few months
to give himself "courage and words" to face his family
over an affair he was having with a black Tortolan girl.
She had wished to have a baby, but he refused because
he felt that he did not make enough money to support
the child. His family had accused the girl of being a
prostitute and of having syphilis. The patient's acute
symptoms came on after the girl had gone back to
Tortola, and were attributed by him to working too
hard and not having enough money to buy sufficient
food.

The French do not fear the physical environment as
do many native Virgin Islanders. The men venture out
to sea in fishing boats and on their farms cope with the
land and the elements. Although the French are highly
quarrelsome and families take one another to court, there
is little physical violence, and that which occurs in usually
associated with alcoholic excess. In general, the French
are held to be lawabiding and respectful of the civil
authorities. Although they had a high rate of tuberculosis,
and seem to have many psychosomatic ailments, they
have availed themselves less of government health services than have the native Virgin Islanders; many use
home remedies, magic potions, and consultation with
obeah men.

---

a strong family system. Women are either part of the system or
definitely out of it. Where familial controls are weak, the system
of prostitution is poorly defined.

Attitudes toward Children

The French are not as sentimental about or as affectionate toward children as native Virgin Islanders, and discipline is generally firmer. The most highly prized quality in a child is its industry, and the main aim in child rearing is to train the child to help the family in making a living. They are more strict about toilet training than natives. Infants are breast-fed and are kept in a hammock near the mother, while the older child may sleep on a mat. Food has long been scarce, and meals emphasize the father's role as provider and serve as a basis for family solidarity. There is considerable difference in the training of boys and girls, although both are expected to work in the home, beginning at about the age of six. Girls are taught to weave straw, while boys learn to make fishing nets and do farm chores. Girls help a great deal with younger siblings (in contrast with many native homes, where children are regarded as too precious to entrust to a youngster). French children go mainly to Catholic parochial schools, but the great majority of boys still do not finish high school. Parents do not equate children's school performance with their own prestige to the extent that native Virgin Islanders do. Boys are allowed much freedom and often get very little supervision, while girls are sheltered and parents actually pay more attention to the education of girls. Compared with the number of native girls who are expelled from school because of pregnancy, very few French girls leave for this reason. This is not only a matter of cultural differ-

ence, but because the Catholic high school is more selec-
tive of its students than the public school system.

Religion

The French are Roman Catholic and are regarded as
devoutly so in that they accept the authority of their
Church without question. The priests and nuns who
teach in the parochial school are from the States and do
not speak French. The French accept Church doctrine
much as they submit to civil authority and seem to regard
dogma much as they recognize that the sky is blue. They
do not structure emotional experience in religious language, nor do they use religious symbols as modes of
adaptation to stress like the native Virgin Islander, who
reads the Bible to overcome loneliness and the fear of
death. Unlike native and British Virgin Islanders, they
do not use church membership as a means of prestige
and as evidence of respectability. Actually, the French
are not articulate on the subject of religion.

Obeah

Yet along with their religion, many of the French are
strong believers in obeah, despite its condemnation by
the priests. The prejudice of the French about Negroes
is often put in terms of obeah. One old Frenchman was
brought to the hospital as a consequence of a quarrel in
which he had accused a native neighbor of "putting"
obeah on him. In the fracas, which resulted from police

intervention, he sustained a compound fracture of his forearm. When he was told that an open reduction would have to be performed, he refused and stated that only the black obeah woman could fix it. (It is unlikely, too, that a Virgin Islander would have shown so much denial of illness.)

The French are not only suspicious of outsiders but often of one another, and obeah furnishes a convenient vehicle for the expression of such feelings. Older people distrust banks and are reputed to hide money under their houses. One couple after having been persuaded to make a deposit in a bank decided to withdraw it after a year. They, however, refused to accept the interest on the money because the additional money might be bewitched.

Psychotic Reactions

Psychotic reactions among the French are mainly of a highly paranoid character and, apart from the alcoholic psychoses, tend to be of long duration. Acute psychotic catatonic episodes, of the type that were observed frequently in Tortolans and natives, were not seen during the course of the study. As a group, they showed much denial of mental illness, patients claiming that they were not crazy and accusing others of being so. Of the sixteen patients, delusions and hallucinations about sex occurred in eleven cases, themes of violence appeared in six, obeah in five, color in four, food in three, and money in three. No French patient had delusions or hallucinations about religion, and in only one instance did the psychotic content pertain to children. Although the French are reputed to be very hypochondriacal, there were no more somatic delusions in their psychoses than there were in those of the other cultural groups.

The sexual ideas most common involved being raped or being otherwise sexually molested. One hospitalized French woman said that men entered her room each night and that the nurses pulled her legs to make her menstruate. Another patient, who was deaf in her left ear, stated that each night a man put his penis in her ear. A male patient confabulated that he was having sexual intercourse with the female nurses, a story that was widely believed in the French community. A patient in a depression attributed his condition to excessive sexual intercourse. Such a high incidence of sexual delusions may be correlated with the great degree to which social roles among the French are differentiated by reason of sex. Sexual symbols serve as handy badges of virtue and are vehicles for the expression of fears, jealousies, and resentments. Delusions about color were often combined with those about sex as in the charge of being raped by a black man. Such delusions about color might be anticipated in view of the way the French differentiate themselves as an ethnic group.

The following case report is illustrative of the occurrence of symbols of sex, color, obeah, violence, and money in the psychoses of French patients:

CASE REPORT

A French woman of twenty-six was first seen in September of 1957. There was a history of recurrent psychotic behavior for eight years, and she had been hospitalized at St. Elizabeth's from 1950 to 1953. The overt illness had begun with alternating states of manic and paranoid expression in which she charged that she had been raped by a Negro and would have a mulatto baby. She had threatened her parents with a machete, and there had been much obscenity and destructive behavior. In 1957 another psychotic episode was characterized by the loudly expressed opinion that a woman was using obeah to make her insane, and there were many stories of sexual assaults by men. She refused medication, saying it was dope, which would kill her, and also refused to eat, saying that the food contained blood, feces, and urine.

When interviewed in 1957, she came to the hospital with her mother. Each woman accused the other of being crazy. The patient charged that she had been mistreated by the mother because she had not been working and had no money to give her. The patient claimed that when she was twelve years old, she had surprised her mother having sexual intercourse with a Negro and the mother had threatened to kill her if she told anyone. There was also much talk of obeah and buried treasure under the house. She was hospitalized and her delusions cleared. She continued to charge that her neighbors bothered her, that the nurses in the hospital were rude and inconsiderate, and that her mother treated her like a child.

After her discharge from the hospital she was seen in the out-patient clinic. She talked mainly about her difficulties in finding a job, about the neighbors calling her crazy, and complained that her mother was too arbitrary with her. After obtaining and losing a job, she attributed her being discharged to a "black woman" and a "white woman" who got rid of her because she knew they had stolen money. She "confessed" to having had a sexual affair with a male patient while in the hospital in a quite dramatic way.

The patient was the only girl of the four living children of a French fisherman. Her parents, natives of St. Barthélemy, had been married for forty-two years and had lost eight children at early ages. Two brothers, fishermen and laborers, lived with the family along with the ten-year-old son of one of them by a native Virgin Islands woman. The patient had had a grade school education, having been withdrawn from the parochial school when the mother thought the nuns did not like the child. The mother was considered as very dominating, suspicious, and overprotective even for a French woman, and the family was said to have been constantly involved in quarrels with the neighbors. The patient had been presumably married to a man from St. Barthélemy, but according to the patient and her mother, she had divorced him because he was an "aunty-man."[2]

During the period of the patient's treatment, her ten-year-old nephew was seen for delinquent behavior. This was described as his attacking members of his family with a knife, cursing and slamming doors, and complaining to his father that he wasn't getting enough to eat. Though this child was quite dark, his grandmother insisted that he was white. She attributed his behavior to being "not right in his head" because he had picked up some money on which a black person had cast a spell. On other occasions she stated that the boy's trouble came from not eating enough.

The patient's mother was also interviewed in connection with her application for a disability pension for rheumatism. In a discussion of her daughter's condition, she claimed it had been brought on by obeah. In her account of her family situation she made many references to sex, food, skin color, money, and witchcraft. She called her son's ex-wives prostitutes and laughingly told of how even at her age her husband was suspicious about her running around.

The following case report illustrates the use of many of the same symbolic themes. It also points up the prob-

2. A local term referring to male homosexuals. The spelling is uncertain and could be "antiman."

lems growing out of the attitudes toward illegitimacy in French society.

CASE REPORT

A thirty-seven-year-old Frenchman was admitted to the psychiatric ward on the issuance of a bench warrant following a complaint by his mother that he had tried to kill her with a knife.

The patient had been born in the French Antilles, illegitimately, and had been brought to the Virgin Islands as an infant. He was raised in a one-room cottage, which his mother rented for a sum of less than one dollar a month. Despite poverty, he was one of the first French children to graduate from high school and attend college. He completed an agricultural course and on his return was fairly successful in this occupation. He Anglicized his name but remained unmarried and continued to live with his mother in her small house. Although regarded as competent, he was said to have become involved in dishonest transactions in which he would forge his mother's name to receipts for material allegedly purchased from her. He worked less and less and for the two years prior to his hospital admission, he refused to leave the house, spending his time lying in bed, smoking cigarettes, drinking coffee, and apparently reading the same books over and over. The local French community were unsympathetic because they felt that he had repudiated them by changing his name. The mother also sought help from the priest, but he would do nothing, as the patient did not attend church. A few weeks before the patient assaulted his mother, he had had an anonymous message sent to her to the effect that he had killed himself.

When seen in the hospital, he was disheveled and unshaven, and was in an excited state. He immediately asked if I were Jewish and went into a long account of a professor at the college he had attended who was "the

son of a famous father," adding that he could not re-
member the name. He then talked at great length about
his own work, of all the commissions he had executed,
and the money he had made. When asked why he had
come to the hospital, he stated, "I like cats and dogs.
I had a bitch from a Greek boat, but we were living too
close to the road. Then I bought a big cat, but it died;
my mother said we'll have to get the kittens. One Sunday
my mother was cooking breakfast, she called me, she
was bleeding where a cat had bitten her. I saw the
teeth marks. I'd read about those South American jungle
cats. I said, 'Do you want me to kill it or give it away?'
Then I saw —— ——, a borderline colored fellow, and
some others in the hibiscus hedge, and then the police
came."

On the following day he demanded in an angry mood
that he be released from the hospital as he was not
crazy. He charged that the hospital authorities were
trying to drive him insane. He compared his predicament
with that of a girl from the States who had been forced
into prostitution.

Over the next few weeks he continued to be paranoid
and demanding. He insisted that he be released from the
hospital so that he could satisfy his "biological urges."
He claimed that he had had sexual intercourse with the
nurses. He said that he was married to a wealthy Puerto
Rican girl from an old distinguished Spanish family,
adding that he also had had intercourse with the girl's
mother. On other occasions he said that he had a wife
in Chicago and that he had been secretly married
several times. (Patient was unmarried. He had dated
girls but, according to informants, he would leave the
house at night only after his mother had fallen asleep.)
He expressed indignation at having to remain on the
same ward with a colored patient who had recently
tried to hang himself. He boasted about his wealth and
offered one thousand dollars for an impartial psychiatric examination. He charged that the staff were trying

to starve him to death. He referred a good deal to race and heredity, pointing out his superiority to the Negro patients and explained that the other white patient on the ward at the time had a hereditary mental illness. He insisted that his mother had lied about his behavior and wanted her brought to the hospital for a mental examination. He accused other members of the French community of having turned her against him. He was particularly bitter about a priest whom he said he had surprised having sexual relations. Further, he pointed out, the priest was committing a mortal sin by using a contraceptive.

His mother visited him at every opportunity bringing food and cigarettes, gifts that must have taken up all of the little income she had from basket making. It was noted that he talked to her only in English and she spoke only in French. She agreed with him that she had been coerced into signing the commitment papers and petitioned for his release.

Although he continued to be supercilious and boastful, his ward behavior improved to the point where he was permitted day passes. On these occasions he simply stayed in his mother's home, despite the tales on his return of sexual exploits. The visits were terminated when his mother charged that he had threatened to kill her, after making her sign a suicide note, if she did not give him several hundred dollars, which he claimed she had buried under the house. The mother's story was denied by the patient. He said he had remained in the house that day and that his mother had seemed very nervous to him. She had kept making excuses to leave, saying she had pains in her stomach, that she had to go to the grocery, and that she had to go out to buy some pork chops. (These were the same excuses that the patient would give when asking to be released from the hospital.) He further claimed that his mother had threatened suicide. Shortly after his return to the hospital, the patient claimed to have swallowed some pills in a suicidal attempt.

This case indicates how one is handicapped by O.W. birth in French society. In the psychosis the patient used symbols of birth, heredity, lineage, and race to represent the problem and as a means of adaptation. Thus he referred to "bitches," to the "son of a famous father," explained mental illness in terms of heredity, and confabulated about having married into a wealthy and distinguished Spanish family. Even the "mortal sin" of the priest was contraception. Because of the culture's attitude toward illegitimacy, the patient and his mother were placed in a position of isolation and extreme emotional dependence on each other. Symbols representing this relationship gave the patient's expressions of inadequacy, resentment, revenge, and self-aggrandizement a particularly valid quality and a great adaptive value. The close identification made with his mother under the circumstances was also reflected in the equivalence of the threats to kill his mother and his suicidal gestures.

The relative absence (one case) of delusions about children reflects the fact that children are not idealized in French society. The French bring up the family more in delusional systems than do Virgin Islanders, indicating its greater status as a source of identity. Except in the cases just cited, these delusions did not involve the mother but rather the father and other relatives. One young woman expressed the embarrassing (for me) delusion that I was her father and had engaged in sexual relationships with her. Another man had the idea that the French people had had his father killed. One woman would hear the voices of her family talking to her, while a man had a long confabulation involving a fishing expedition with his brother-in-law.

Delusions about food were recorded in three of the

sixteen psychotic cases. The content did not differ from the ideas frequently expressed by the relatives of patients. For example, the wife of one Frenchman indicated her resentment toward his family by claiming that they had accused her of deliberately poisoning the patient. In another instance, an infant was admitted to the hospital in a toxic state as a result of having swallowed rat poison. The child's family promptly attributed the poisoning to some Puerto Rican neighbors with whom they had quarreled about some goats wandering into the yard.

In contrast to native and British Virgin Islanders, French patients did not have delusions about religion. This correlates with the observation that the French do not express their feelings in religious terms or conceive of the ideals of conduct in a religious context. Feelings of fear, hostility, and revenge seem to be experienced more vividly through expressions of belief in obeah. Delusions and hallucinations about obeah were encountered in five patients.

In summary, the French are a distinct, homogeneous group who gain a great deal of identity through ethnic origin, family, language, and their position as a white minority in a largely Negro population. Family organization is based on marriage, and illegitimacy is a disgrace. There is a marked differentiation of social and economic roles on the basis of gender. There has been a high degree of endogamous marriage, and family feuds are common. Belief in obeah is strong. Psychotic reactions are mainly paranoid in type with a high incidence of delusions and hallucinations about sex, violence, color, food, and obeah.

10 THE PUERTO RICANS

THE MAJORITY of the 8,000 or so Puerto
Ricans in the Virgin Islands live in St. Croix, whence they
have emigrated from Vieques. They have preserved a great
deal of group identity, and Spanish remains their only
or preferred language. Although Puerto Ricans form almost half of the population of St. Croix, many do not
speak English and very few Crucians have learned
Spanish. They tend to form their own community and to
keep up customs like cock-fighting. Puerto Rican separate-
ness has been recently underscored by the formation of
a political party dedicated to the furthering of Puerto
Rican interests in the Virgin Islands. As in the mainland
United States there is animosity toward Puerto Ricans by
Crucians on the expressed grounds of their clannishness,
quick-tempered violence, and unsanitary habits. There

is also a feeling among Crucians that the economic progress of Puerto Rican shopkeepers has been at the expense of native Virgin Islanders. On some hospital wards, where the nursing staff is native and many of the patients Puerto Rican, antagonisms may occur.

As compared with native Virgin Islanders, Puerto Ricans are not as conscious of social position, and, regardless of education and wealth, they seem to associate freely and volubly with one another. There is a high degree of family solidarity, and when an immigrant from Vieques establishes himself, he usually sends for his family. In contrast to Virgin Islanders, family feeling even seems to include girls working as domestics in the homes. On visits to the hospital, a Puerto Rican patient is generally accompanied by a member of his family, especially if he does not speak English well. Puerto Ricans are very sensitive to insults, or supposed insults, concerning their families, particularly mothers, sisters, wives, and girl friends. Another aspect of a family-based identification is that, while Virgin Islanders generally will welcome any child into their home, Puerto Ricans much prefer a blood relative, so that the foster-home program has been more successful among natives than Puerto Ricans.

Family Organization

The family organization of Puerto Ricans in the Virgin Islands has aspects of both the French nuclear family structure and the household system common among lower-class native Virgin Islanders and Tortolans. There are both father-headed family units and O.W. unions. A study in 1947 by Clarence Senior in St. Croix estimated the number of consensual relationships as slightly under the figures for Crucians. There do not seem to be the "grandmother households" or as many female-controlled units as among native Virgin Islanders. A Puerto Rican woman living in an extramarital relationship is apt to pay lip service to the institution of marriage. She may say she is married or give some excuse, such as that she can't marry the man with whom she is living because she is married and divorce is against her religion. In the home the father is regarded as supreme. His needs come first, and the fact that he works and provides the family with a living confers great prestige. Puerto Rican women are expected to defer to their husbands, and they take on more of a suffering martyr role than do native Virgin Islanders. Grandparents are part of the family unit and expect to be cared for by the wealthiest child.

Attitudes toward Children

Puerto Rican parents are very affectionate with children. They fondle them a great deal, referring to them as *precioso* and gifts of God. They greatly prize a child who is *simpàtico*, that is, amiable and cheerful. The physical appearance of a child is very important, with a small, round face, light skin, and curly hair being esteemed. Children may be named in accordance with their looks, like "Bonita" and "Negrita." Discipline is enforced by scolding, coaxing, and much cursing and abusive language. Systematic whippings are uncommon, physical punishment generally consisting of a slap. Young children run around naked, toilet training is casual, and there is no concern about masturbation. A male baby's sexual parts are considered cute, parents boast about the size of a boy's penis, and fondle and caress the genitals.[1]

In the raising of children there is considerable differentiation in terms of age and sex. The eldest child gets many prerogatives, his needs being second only to those of the father. Boys get more privileges in the home, and obedience is stressed more in girls, who have many household duties to perform, such as caring for the younger children. It is important for boys not to be weaklings and to defend their rights, particularly in the matter of not letting girls get the better of them.[2] Puerto Ricans do not seem to be as eager as native Virgin Islanders for their children to be educated, in part, possibly, because only English is used in the schools. Intelligence is accepted as an alternative to beauty, but is less encouraged in girls than in boys. There is more truancy among Puerto Ricans than Crucians. There is no concealment about sexual matters, which are discussed freely in the home with many joking allusions and teasing among the men. After twelve, however, girls are rather closely guarded. It is customary for a boy and girl of fifteen or sixteen to "elope" together and then return to live in the home of one of the families, usually that of the girl. If they approve of the boy and all get along well, then the couple remain and eventually may get married.

1. My attention to this feature was drawn when a jealous six-year-old girl tried to cut off her younger brother's penis with the top of a powder can. In another case a mother dramatically began an interview by exposing her eleven-year-old son's penis and announcing that his enuresis demanded an operation on it.

2. Recently gangs of Puerto Rican boys living together have been involved in a series of robberies in St. Croix.

Food and Work

Food is an extremely important element in social relationships and in maintaining the identity of Puerto Ricans. To the dismay of the medical authorities, many cling to their diet of beans and rice, and white rice at that. Puerto Rican patients in the hospital often won't eat, and food is brought in by their relatives. (To the casual observer it doesn't look any different from that eaten by natives.) In the home the woman's primary task is to prepare meals for her family and to wait on her husband and his friends. Women take pride in their ability as cooks; and casual visitors, even in very poor homes, are offered coffee, tea, or something to eat. I recall visiting a wealthy contractor at 9 P.M. one evening and being served a large quantity of fried fish by his wife, who spent the time cooking in the kitchen. In St. Croix a greater proportion of Puerto Ricans than Crucians live in the country, and after accumulating some money the aim is to move to town and open a grocery store. This establishment will be maintained by the labor of the whole family.

Puerto Ricans take pride in hard work, and men feel that their prestige is bound up in having a job, even a menial one as an agricultural laborer. A Puerto Rican will work long hours at a hard job, where a Crucian may feel the time put in is not worth the money or is not commensurate with his dignity. Women will work in a family store, but do not do domestic labor outside of the home. There is more of the idea that "woman's place is in the home" than in native society. The equating of work with manhood, or *machismo*, enters into the way Puerto Ricans structure illness. In general, they are less attentive to headaches and minor complaints than Virgin Islanders. They are apt, though, to express their feelings of incapacity by complaining of being "too sick to work" and point out how hard they could work if they were well.[3]

Expression of Violence

Puerto Ricans are more emotionally demonstrative than most Virgin Islanders, who generally keep a more dignified aspect. They speak a staccato Spanish with a great deal of smiling, laughing, and other gestures. In taking clinical histories one is struck by the way patients may have a smiling, happy, animated demeanor even when describing how someone tried to kill them. They form relationships on a very personal level with overt expressions of warm affection and revengeful hate. They become jealous, particularly about women and the home, and like Virgin Islanders are sensitive to slights and insults. These, however, call for action, often with knives or machetes. There is less fear of physical combat than among natives, and the display of aggression is usually quite dramatic. The behavior of women at funerals is also histrionic. Puerto Ricans also bear grudges for a long time and these may even lead to murder. Yet on the

3. A study by Stycos of Puerto Ricans on the mainland of Puerto Rico listed the qualities regarded by men as making up *machismo*. In order, these were honesty and reliability; conquering women sexually; fighting, boasting, and gambling; working hard; performing community and family duties; honor and chivalry; and courage. Having children was not mentioned.

whole, despite their use of violence, the Puerto Ricans are not as quarrelsome as the French and many natives. Law-enforcement officials feel that Puerto Ricans have respect for the law after finding that authorities cannot be easily bribed, and the felony rate of Puerto Ricans is not significantly higher than that for Crucians.

Religion, Death, and Obeah

In religion Puerto Ricans are Roman Catholic or Lutheran or belong to one of the Pentecostal sects. Many of the Catholics seem only nominally religious, especially the men, who go to church only for weddings and funerals. Only the Pentecostals seem to structure moral issues in religious terms, and only they try to "live by the Bible." Recently, there was a serious discussion in one of the Pentecostal groups as to whether a psychotic member should be treated by prayer or sent to the hospital. The Puerto Rican Catholics do not seem as preoccupied with religious images of death and martyrdom as are people in other Latin American countries, such as Mexico. Belief in obeah is widespread among Puerto Ricans in the Virgin Islands regardless of religious affiliation.

Psychotic Reactions

Apart from frank psychoses, suicide and suicidal gestures are much more common in Puerto Ricans than among Virgin Islanders. Of the five suicides that occurred in the Virgin Islands to my knowledge during the time of this study, three of the persons were Puerto

Rican, one Continental, and one native. Several women, jealous or angry about love affairs, poured kerosene on themselves and ignited it. Others swallowed lysol in suicidal gestures. In a comparable situation a Virgin Island woman would be more apt to do nothing, engage in verbal abuse, or go to court. Puerto Ricans are apt to make dramatic threats of suicide in stressful situations. For example, a man after being denied a relief grant threatened to kill himself and his family. Others were certain that their families would starve to death.

The following is an example of the use of such symbols under stress:

CASE REPORT

A twenty-one-year-old man serving a prison term for burglary and statutory rape was seen psychiatrically following a putative suicidal attempt by hanging. He had been born in Vieques and had lived there for a few years with his mother. He then moved to Fajardo with his father and had come to St. Croix to rejoin his mother nine years previously. He was illiterate and had worked as a fisherman. For the past year he had been living with a twelve-year-old girl, to whom he referred as his wife, and her mother and stepfather. The patient denied the suicidal attempt but charged that the prison personnel were trying to kill him and starve him to death. He also reported many dreams of people trying to kill him. He said he knew that the food was poisoned because he could not digest it properly. He spontaneously talked of his childhood, saying that his mother had left him because he was bad. He also went on about how badly his mother had treated him as a child.

In prison, the patient was a difficult disciplinary problem, not being motivated by the usual rewards and punishments. Though illiterate, he was not mentally deficient in the ordinary sense of the term and did not appear severely depressed. In his reaction to the stress of imprisonment, he expresses his feelings in metaphors of being killed, starved, and poisoned and in language about his mother treating him badly. It seemed from the history that the patient's most intense emotional experiences had occurred in these symbolic areas, and it is not surprising that his "reality" should have been structured in such a representation of his environment.

In psychotic reactions, the theme of physical attack appeared in the delusions and hallucinations of fifteen patients of the twenty-two studied. Most frequently, the patient reported attempts of people to kill him with knives, machetes, or guns. Two of the women claimed their husbands were trying to kill them. In some cases, patients stated fictitiously that other people had been killed. One man early in his psychotic reaction went to the police and confabulated that he had stabbed a man (another Puerto Rican). Another man insisted to the police that he knew the killer in an unsolved St. Croix murder mystery. A patient who had recurrent psychotic disturbances associated with drinking would inaugurate each episode by exposing his chest and goading men into a knife duel. It is important to recognize that such talk and acting out of violence is not simply an expression of hostility but an indication of the part that a show of violence plays in *machismo* and the social role of men. It is of interest that in the psychotic reactions in each cultural group, violence was almost universally attributed to men.

As has been indicated, the ideas of food being poisoned or of being deliberately starved to death were recurrent themes in psychotic reactions and other situations of stress. These were prominent in seven cases. One man claimed that his mother had poisoned his food, while others felt that their husbands or wives or the nurses in the hospital were plotting to poison them and would refuse to eat. This high incidence of delusions and hallucinations about food accords with the important role of eating in Puerto Rican social patterns.

Delusions and hallucinations about religion occurred in three cases among the Puerto Ricans. One man claimed that he was God and that people were trying to kill him by draining all of his blood. Another man with epileptic seizures heard God telling him the winning number in the lottery. Ideas of obeah were expressed by five patients. One woman claimed that a man had been killed by an obeah man's powder having been dropped into his coffee, and she accused another man of having killed her mother by planting an animal in her belly. When this patient became more rational, she suggested that her illness had either been caused by a woman putting something in front of her house or from having gotten tired out from too much washing and ironing. Another patient accused her husband of having had an affair with a woman in the yard and practising obeah on her through a bottle.

Delusions about children were not common in the Puerto Rican group, occurring in only one case, but the subject sometimes came up in other instances, particularly in terms of a child being starved. For example, a man of forty-five, who had been convicted on a charge of molesting a child sexually, expressed as his chief concern his fear that his children might starve while he was in jail. In another case a man charged that his son was not really his, but this was not classed as a delusion about children. While one would expect fewer delusions about children in the French and Puerto Ricans because of the lesser degree of adult identity gained through children, the extremely low incidence is partly accounted for by the fact that the French and Puerto Rican patient groups were predominantly male.

As in the French group, there was more implication of family members in the delusional systems (six cases) than there was among native Virgin Islanders (eight cases) and Tortolans (none). Whereas the French delusions and hallucinations were more commonly about the father, those of Puerto Ricans predominantly concerned their mothers. Three patients had the idea that their mother had been killed, while an epileptic reported hearing a voice saying he had killed his mother. Apart from psychoses, patients talked a good deal about their mothers, especially about their illnesses and hardships. They frequently spoke of dreaming about their mothers, and the complaint that Mother had treated the patient badly or had not loved him was common. These features may be linked to the way the mother is idealized as a loving, devoted, and often suffering figure in Puerto Rican culture. One's own feelings of being abused and mistreated may be vividly symbolized in such a cultural stereotype.

Two patients had delusions about the government. One man claimed that he had sold his vote to the Independistas for ten thousand dollars and that they had a microphone outside of his window recording all of his statements. Another offered a confabulation about President Eisenhower having promised him a large sum of money. In reference to money and property, the subject came up most frequently in the delusions and hallucinations of Continentals with no significant differences in the incidence among native Virgin Islanders, French, and Puerto Ricans.

The following case report is illustrative of the use of many of the symbols common in psychotic reactions in the Puerto Rican group:

CASE REPORT

A forty-five-year-old skilled laborer, a member of the Church of God, was hospitalized on the tuberculosis ward following a sudden hemoptysis. Several days later he became restless and talked a great deal of religion and killing people. He refused medication, claiming that he would be healed by faith, and he burned incense to keep away evil spirits. The patient began the interview in an affable way by asking for my autograph and expressed his pleasure at meeting so distinguished a person. He then produced a drawing he had made of the way he had fallen off a roof while building the hospital several years ago (true). He told of his work attainments and how St. Thomians were jealous of him because he was such a hard worker. He then told of his mother's long illness with ulcers and how his own ulcers had been cured. Because of his mother's death, he had had to leave school, but as a child he had been so smart they had jumped him from the first to the third grade. His father had died of pneumonia, and he described this as a "wound in my heart."

When asked about his symptoms and the reason for hospitalization, he told of having a cavity in his left lung which he thought had been caused by some men in a bar jumping on him and kicking him in the chest. He felt that he had been badly treated on the ward, that the nurses intentionally put dirt in his food, and that they had "lots of tricks with laughs and looks" when the doctor comes around.

In this case the stress is compounded of the implications of the acute physical illness and the loss of integrity and status in the hospital situation. The fact that the nurses were not Puerto Rican was an additional factor. In his psychotic reaction, he adapts to the stress by representing the illness and other events in language that expresses "reality" most exquisitely and vividly for him. Such a sense of reality and identity is achieved in part because such symbols as work, food, violence, religion, and obeah subserve significant social patterns in his culture. In references to the illnesses of his mother and father he can talk of his own illness in a way as to give it substance and meaning and make it lose its quality of, for him, nameless dread. After one psychiatric interview, this patient made an excellent recovery, and one can regard the psychosis as a therapeutic procedure.

Delusions about sex occurred in four of the twenty patients, in three of the six women and in one of the men. The man, a prisoner, accused other inmates of trying to have homosexual relations with him. The women gave delusional accounts of the sexual activities of their husbands. There were several other accusations of marital infidelity of a spouse, but the veracity of the story could not be ascertained. Whether delusional or not in the sense of true or false, such ideas were significant ways of expressing feelings and interpreting the environment.

Conversion Hysteria

This subject is treated in this section because five of the eight cases in which a diagnosis was made were Puerto Rican. The other patients were Continental, Crucian, and French, respectively. The category of conversion hysteria is limited to cases of motor and sensory paralysis, and abnormal movements and postures. Three patients had a hemiplegia and hemisensory syndrome; in another, no cause could be found for an expressed inability to move a leg, and in the fifth instance the patient had attacks of bizarre movements. The diagnosis was not made in the group of Virgin Islanders. One woman from Tortola complained of having no feeling in the right side of her head, and another claimed that she could not swallow because of a snake in her throat, but in each case a catatonic picture soon developed. These might have been classed as hysterical episodes. In any view, it would be of interest to learn if the classical versions of conversion hysteria in a culture bear any relationship to the degree to which physical violence is a preferred channel of communication and symbolizes virility.

Summing up, Puerto Ricans gain a great deal of identity through ethnic grouping and the family. The patterns of family organization and the differentiation of social roles by sex occupy a position intermediate between the patriarchal, nuclear family system of the French and the extended household arrangements of many lower-class Virgin Islanders. The forming of stereotypes about mothers rather than children is reflected in the observation that psychotic Puerto Ricans more frequently are deluded about their mothers than they are about children. Symbols of violence, food, sex, and obeah are important elements in patterns of social relatedness and these themes are prominent in the content of psychotic reactions.

11 CONCLUDING NOTES

THIS CHAPTER will review and comment on the correlations that have been made among cultural values, that is, preferred channels of relatedness, and the content of psychoses in the groups studied in the Virgin Islands. On the basis of these findings, some more generalized features of the relationship of culture to delusional content and other methods of adapting to stress will be discussed and some applications to clinical psychiatry considered.

Symbolism of Children

The highest incidence of delusions, confabulations, and hallucinations about children was noted among British and American Virgin Islanders and the lowest in the French and Puerto Rican groups. One would expect to find many delusions about children among a people who express their needs and feelings in terms of children and who use such stereotyped conceptions of children to furnish a basis of identity. The Virgin Islander, to a great extent, perceives the environment as if he were a helpless, disobedient, "bad" or "good" child. In situations of stress particularly, he carries out these roles in his own actions and in his anticipation and expectation of the behavior of others. In delusions and hallucinations it is significant that when the age of the "child" was specified, it proved to be an infant or very young child.[1]

We have spoken of delusions as cultural stereotypes, and among Virgin Islanders a stereotyped conception of children often seems to be a substitute for more personal and individualized relationships between adults and children. The great majority of parents work outside of the home, and a large share of child care is carried out by relatives, friends, and maids. When parents are with their children, they often seem to be making up their own absence and deficiencies by overindulgence or insistence on proper behavior and arbitrary discipline far exceeding that imposed by the adult on himself. Despite the tradition of great love for children, there is a tremendous discrepancy between the expressed ideal and what is ac-

1. One might apply this concept to the attitudes of Virgin Islanders to the federal government. Many people seem to have the belief that the government has given a lot of money for the children of the Virgin Islands and that the local welfare authorities have only to distribute it. Many of the French feel that old persons are entitled to a pension with much less emphasis on children.

tually done for children. Despite years of effort on the part of United States Public Health Service personnel, the expenditure of many thousands of dollars in federal funds, and the numerous conferences on child care attended, there is still no satisfactory program for retarded children in the Virgin Islands.

The French, on the other hand, are not sentimental about children and raise them more rigorously. A child gains recognition as a participant in the economic life of the family, and his activities are seen in the context of family tradition and purpose. While Puerto Ricans are very affectionate toward their children, the child does not serve as a source of identity as it does for Virgin Islanders. Among Puerto Ricans, the sentimentality is rather about mothers. The Puerto Rican child is esteemed for its good looks and brightness, but pregnancies are often unwanted for economic reasons. Among Virgin Islanders, particularly from the British Islands, children are welcome regardless of economic circumstances and may even be regarded as insurance for one's old age.

One would expect to find many delusions about children in the matricentric societies of the West Indies, where the major emotional relationship is between parent and child. The absence of the father from many homes increases the dependence of the child and mother on each other. Often, it seems that it is not the physical absence that matters so much but that a stereotype of the father as a strict, brutal, or irresponsible person complementing that of the helpless child is built up so readily. Poverty adds to the picture in that the father does not gain the prestige that comes with a well-paying job. It is in turn true that the social conditions tend to produce character traits which are not conducive to economic success. Thus psychological, social, and economic factors are intimately related.

The symbolism of children is of course not confined to economically deprived societies but is common in many segments of American culture. A study of psychotic content relating to children noted the theme in thirty of one hundred and forty patients with confabulations and delusions. Such patients talked about nonexistent "phantom" children, ascribed their own incapacities to a real or imaginary child, or expressed their own fears and putative feelings of helplessness in terms of a "child" being mistreated, neglected, kidnapped, raped, or killed. In considering the family background of the patients, one parent seemed to have predominated. As adults these patients had formed their most important social relationships either by taking the conventionally defined role of a child or placing others in it. They were described by informants as having been very "emotional" about children; many were characterized as dependent and "childish," while others were pictured as dominating, worrisome, and wrapped up in their own children's lives. In all instances, stereotyped attitudes toward children had given a unifying purpose and direction to a wide range of acts and motives.

Symbolism of Food

The infrequency of delusions about food among St. Thomians and the high incidence in the French and Puerto Rican groups suggest that psychotic content dealing with food would occur frequently in cultures where

activities centered about food were important components of social patterns. In such a culture the family unit
would be the eating unit and the roles of various family
members would be defined to a considerable extent in
connection with the acquisition, dispensing, and consum-
ing of food. Similarly, changes in status might be denoted
by changes in eating habits. In French and most Puerto
Rican families, only the father is the "breadwinner" and
his authority and status are expressed in this role. The
composition of the eating group parallels the family
group, whereas among Virgin Islanders a person may live
in one household and get his meals from another. Also,
children commonly eat irregularly and often prepare and
even buy food for themselves.

Other aspects of food symbolism would include food
taboos and rules about who may eat with whom. There
would be great faith in the efficacy of certain diets in the
maintenance of health and strength. Abstaining from
certain foods at certain times would have moral and
religious connotations. Such a society would have its
"national" dishes. Few, if any, of these features prevail
in St. Thomian society. Even the Catholic Church permits the eating of meat on Fridays on the grounds that
food is scarce in the Virgin Islands.

The circumstance of the relative scarcity and great
expense of food in St. Thomas brings up the theoretical
point of the relationship of physical and biological factors to the social patterns involving food. Much of the
older material in the literature on the symbolism of food
considers the subject in terms of the frustration of the
hunger drive and the evolving of secondary drives based
on hunger. Holmberg in a fascinating account of his experiences with the Siriono Indians of Bolivia describes a

primitive, technologically impoverished society dominated by the quest for food. There is hoarding of food and
reluctance to share it. Nothing but food is stolen, and
quarrels are about food rather than about sex or property.
While sex play is public, the people are apt to sneak off
into the forest to eat. Loss of appetite is a sign of impending death, and sick people eat tremendously.

Holmberg considers these patterns of behavior as expressions of a frustrated hunger drive. Yet the very idea
that food is scarce is a relative one, and the classification
of "food" is arbitrarily made by the culture. Actually, the
Siriono seem to have eaten huge quantities of meat and
to have not regarded edible palms, nuts, grubs, and
worms as food. The Siriono dream about food, eat when
they are frightened and anxious, and express aggression,
affection, jealousy, and other feelings through food not
only because they are hungry but because food is a major
source of identity in a society marked by the absence of
ritual, ceremony, magic, and religion, and in which pride
in race, land, and property are absent.

Another interesting account of the involvement of food
in social patterns is given by Audrey Richards in a study
of a Bantu society in South Africa. She describes how
"the emotional bonds of human kinship are intimately
dependent on a whole complex of institutions by which
food is distributed, shared and produced in a particular
community." Richards does not give any information concerning the incidence of delusions about food in psychotic reactions, but Laubscher, who studied Bantu tribes
in the Union of South Africa, treats the subject. He
describes a "cattle" culture with numerous food ceremonies involving slaughtering, eating, giving, and barter-
ing. Certain parts of an animal are eaten by men, others
by women, and different foods figure in different cere-

monies. One always offers food to a visitor, and if it is not proferred, stealing is justified. Brides are purchased for cattle, and in negotiations the girl is referred to as "cattle." In such conversations the color of each ox and cow is described, and a woman's way of rejecting a suitor is to drive his cattle away. In psychotic reactions the most frequently expressed delusion of grandeur concerns cattle. The most common delusion of persecution among women is of being poisoned, while in men ideas of food poisoning are exceeded only by those of being bewitched.

Food is an important symbolic element not only in primitive, predominantly agricultural societies, but in advanced urban cultures as well. It is hardly surprising that delusions about food should be so common in psychoses. In a comparison of the delusional systems of lower-class Neapolitans and middle- and upper-class Americans, Anne Parsons found delusions and fears of poisoning to be frequent in each group. The very fact that such delusions are regarded as cardinal symptoms of a psychosis attests to the significance of the symbol in the culture.

Symbolism of Sex

It was found that sexual themes occurred frequently in the psychotic reactions of the French and were relatively uncommon among Virgin Islanders, with Puerto Ricans occupying an intermediate position on the scale. From this distribution one would anticipate many sexual delusions and hallucinations in cultures where there is a classification of the environment in sexual terms and a marked differentiation of social roles according to biological gender. In such cultures, as exemplified by the French and Puerto Ricans, one gains a great deal of identity in terms of "masculinity" and "femininity," there is much emphasis on sex in interpersonal relationships, and sexual attitudes and actions are equated with ethical values such as sin and virtue. By these criteria, Virgin Islands society is not "sex oriented" despite the great deal of physical sexual activity. Men do not gain special status by reason of gender. They are not noticeably more aggressive than women, and sexual features are not prominent in moral codes.

The point is made that in "sex-oriented" societies the probable high incidence of sexual delusions does not mean that they are the manifestations of the loss of control of biological drives or instincts, or a regression to infantile styles of sexual expression. A recent study (Weinstein and Kahn, 1961) of delusions and other disturbances of sexual behavior following brain injury, conditions under which "loss of control" and "regression" should be eminently facilitated, showed that such behavior appeared only in patients of a particular social background. These patients came from families in which attitudes and motives had to a large degree been structured in stereotyped concepts of masculinity and femininity, and the roles of father and mother sharply differentiated. It made no difference whether the patient had "suppressed" his sexual feelings or expressed them openly. What mattered was that in either instance interpersonal events had been interpreted in a sexual context.

Symbolic Aspects of Race and Color

Delusions and hallucinations involving the designation of skin color figured most prominently among the French and were least common in St. Thomians. While the French, to a great degree, structure their social environment in terms of skin color, for native Virgin Islanders color is descriptive rather than classificatory and the term "Negro" is not the social category that it is in other parts of the United States. It would be expected that Negroes in the continental United States, where color is classificatory, would have a higher incidence of delusions and hallucinations about color than those living in the Virgin Islands. Also, such delusions would occur in persons, white or Negro, whose major system of identity was defined in terms of race and color. While Virgin Islanders may esteem light color and "good" hair, the classificational requisite for delusional formation is lacking.

Symbolism of Religion

Religious delusions and hallucinations appeared most frequently among British Virgin Islanders from the "Holy Island" of Tortola, and least commonly in the French. These findings were in accord with expectations for Tortolans who express feelings and moral values in terms of religion. The lack of religious delusions among the French was initially a surprise, as they are considered to be devout Roman Catholics. Their devoutness, however, consists of accepting the authority of their priests much as they accept civil law and authority. They do not structure their environment in religious categories or use religious symbols as modes of adaptation to stress.

While the French are Catholic and the majority of British Virgin Islanders are Protestant, the difference in the incidence of religious delusions is not only a matter of religious denomination. In the Windward Island of St. Lucia, where the population is almost wholly Roman Catholic and speaks a French patois, I found many religious delusions expressed by patients in the mental hospital, far outnumbering ideas about obeah. Crowley has observed that religious values permeate St. Lucian life. The Church administers schools and welfare, and each village has shrines used for daily prayer. Celebrations and rituals mark the passing of time and changes in age and status of the inhabitants, and mundane activities acquire divine sanction. There are no less than twenty-five annual religious festivals and holidays in St. Lucia, including special days for laundresses, fishermen, and chauffeurs. Even the buses in Castries bear religious mottoes.

A correlation of cultural values and psychotic delusions about religion was made by Stainbrook in Bahia. Lower-class rural patients interpreted fear, anxiety, and retribution as arising from cultural deities, African or Catholic. Both megalomaniac and persecutory symptoms were expressed in terms of cultural, religious institutions. Middle-class men, whose position in the social scale was characterized by less involvement in religion, had psychotic delusions more concerned with economic and class conceptions of power.

The religious practices and language of British and American Virgin Islanders are highly reminiscent of those described for eighteenth- and nineteenth-century England and Scotland, the provenience of most of the white settlers. This may be related to an interesting study made by Klaf and Hamilton in which they compared the incidence of religious preoccupations in schizophrenic patients admitted to the Bethlem Royal Hospital in the

period 1853–1862 with those admitted in the decade
1950–1960. They found that three times as many male
and female acute schizophrenics had religious preoccupations in the nineteenth-century subjects as compared with
the twentieth-century group. The authors correlate the
reduced incidence with the change in the position of
religion in British life and thought. The study also found
that there were twice as many patients with sexual preoccupations in the twentieth-century admissions, indicating the role of cultural determination in that area.

Obeah

It is commonly stated that witchcraft is a means of
channeling aggression and relieving tension, and there
are reports that the practise increases during periods of
stress and insecurity (Kluckhohn) (Carpenter). Yet the
validity of the symbol for the individual depends on how
it fits into a social pattern and reinforces identity. The
accounts of African witchcraft given by Nadel emphasize
that its practises represent aspects of the organization of
the society. Among the Nupe, witches were exclusively
female in a society dominated economically by women
traders. In other groups accusations of witchcraft were
made only by persons in a particular family relationship,
and Nadel believed that it was causally related to the
stresses associated with specific kinship ties. As Kluckhohn indicated in his study of the Navajo, witchcraft is
generally attributed to members of one's own group
rather than to outsiders, which would be the case if it
were only a matter of labeling malevolent forces.

The observation that many of the same delusions were

expressed by nonpsychotic relatives of the patient brings up the question of the relationship of such delusional systems to psychoses. Despite the fact that many members of the community held the same ideas about obeah and the supernatural that the patient had, there was generally no disagreement with the psychiatrist's evaluation as to when a psychosis existed. Regardless of their belief in obeah, the families' definition of the social limits of normality corresponded with my own. Anne Parsons reports that the same situation existed in respect to witchcraft in Naples.

It has been said that the normal behavior of one culture can be a psychotic manifestation in another. Cases are cited where people belonging to cultures recognizing witchcraft have been mistakenly hospitalized by psychiatrists unfamiliar with such practises. For example, Hallowell (1938) tells of a Negro committed to a mental hospital and thought to be suffering from private delusions, after which it was discovered that he belonged to a local religious cult of which his ideology was characteristic. Actually, such reports are highly anecdotal and poorly documented. They rely on personal communication and second- and third-hand quotes, and the original cases have not been recorded in systematic fashion. In retrospect, the physicians who hospitalized the Negro with his delusions and the Neapolitan who talked about witchcraft were probably quite correct in their diagnoses. Further, the expression of belief in witchcraft by Neapolitans or the relating of visions by members of religious cults cannot be accepted as compatible with mental health simply because they exist in a culture. The evaluation of such behavior in terms of whether it is psychotic or not depends on how it is used in social transactions. For example, many Americans believe that fluoridization of drinking water is a Communist poisoning plot. Yet, such a person, however firmly he holds his belief or however vigorously he may join in organizations to prevent fluoridization, is not regarded as psychotic. But, if he takes the idea as a condensed symbol of all his problems and uncertainties, if he regards everyone with whom he might feel anxious as a Communist agent, or if he prevents fellow office workers from taking a drink of water, then he might be considered psychotic.

Symbolism of Death

The high incidence of delusions and hallucinations among British Virgin Islanders may be correlated with the symbolic significance of death in the culture. For Tortolans, the great fear of death and the many beliefs and superstitions about death and spirits help structure relationships in the environment into meaningful and orderly patterns. The physical event of death is integrated into a social institution, and funerals are more important events than marriages. In the psychoses of British Virgin Islanders symbols of death were differentiated from ideas of assault and killing. The characteristic psychotic reaction involved both verbal and physical symbols of death in an acute stuporous episode, with mute immobility punctuated by talk of spirits and death. When Tortolans in hallucinations heard their relatives speak to them, the "voices" were generally those of deceased relatives.

Symbolism of Violence

In the psychotic reactions of all the cultural groups in the study, themes of violence were prominent, with little intergroup difference. This suggests that a great many cultures structure their environment in terms of fear and violence and that such symbols are of predominant importance in the defining of interpersonal relationships and the achievement of identity. It seemed to make little difference for the content of psychoses whether the symbols were mainly verbal as in St. Thomians or more physical as in Puerto Ricans. Put another way, it did not seem to matter greatly if physical aggression was "suppressed," as one might assume about St. Thomians, or released impulsively, as is habitual with Puerto Ricans.

Symbolic Content and Clinical Category

With three or four exceptions all patients with psychotic reactions were of lower-class status. This does not mean necessarily that psychoses occurred in these exact proportions in the total population, because patients from upper-class families might be treated by private physicians or taken to Puerto Rico or the States. Yet I got the impression that psychotic pictures were more common in the lower class as defined in this study. The project was not designed to compare the degree of stress in upper- and lower-class groups or to measure the resources for coping with it. It may be, however, that at lower educational and socioeconomic levels, reality is generally experienced in more stereotyped fashion, and under stress problems are more readily represented in the conventional and highly condensed symbols of delusions and hallucinations.

The study suggests that it is fruitful to consider the relationship of culture to mental illness and problems of nosology in terms of symbolic content. Much of the literature has been concerned with the question as to whether clinical entities like schizophrenia appear in particular cultures. In recent years there have been a number of statements that classical depressions do not occur in many cultures, particularly the less technologically developed ones of Asia and Africa (Wittkower and Fried). Among Virgin Islanders, so-called classical depressions with ideas of self-derogation, failure, and suicide are rare. It will be of interest, then, to compare Virgin Islanders with an English-speaking group of comparable size and uniqueness, in whom depressions with obsessive rumination over omission and sin, sometimes leading to suicide, is the most common type of reaction to stress. Such a group are the Hutterites, whose social patterns, as described by Eaton and Weil, are radically different from those of Virgin Islanders. The Hutterites, a Protestant religious sect akin to the Mennonites and Amish, live in farming communities in the Dakotas, Manitoba, and Alberta. They have a strong nuclear family system based on marriage with emphasis on kinship ties and obligations to the community. Male authority prevails, and status is enhanced with age. Work is positively valued, and, along with a high degree of material prosperity, there is a tradition of austere simplicity and poverty. American values are rejected rather than imitated, and there is a principle of self-sufficiency. Religious values, as in the Virgin

Islands, are important in the conduct of everyday life, but religion is less authoritarian, as judged by the fact that ministers are chosen from the group.

The significant factors that differentiate Hutterite from native Virgin Islands society in respect to shaping mental illness in the form of depression seem to be in the way work and accomplishment are symbolized and the way in which such values related the person in his group. When Virgin Islanders do become depressed, they do not talk of their failures nor do they reproach themselves for failure to carry out their obligations toward others. Rather, depressive feelings are expressed in the symbols of religion, sin, and death, and attitudes toward children.

If the definition of depression as a clinical syndrome is made sufficiently broad, it is likely that no culture is immune. Disputing the claim that depressions are rare among Africans, Field noted that in rural Ghana, women commonly become depressed, accompanied by self-accusations of witchcraft. The content of depressions varies with the symbolic values of a culture, and "classical depression" is one of the varieties.

While catatonic psychoses were common among Virgin Islanders, particularly those from the British islands, they were rare among the French, who, instead, showed a high incidence of paranoid reactions. The explanation involves both cultural factors and the matter of our psychiatric nosology. We generally class as "paranoid" those psychoses in which the environment is structured in personal terms with its malevolent and powerful forces wielded by people. Paranoid delusional systems usually involve ideas of power and influence, sex, food, money, race, and heredity. All these symbols lend themselves well to interpersonal representation. The importance of symbols of sex, food, and race in French culture ensures that they will be involved in psychotic reactions. In Virgin Islands culture, on the other hand, symbols of death and religion are paramount; and in psychotic reactions, the environment is represented in terms of God, the supernatural, spirits, and the afterworld rather than in the actions of other persons or groups of persons. Also, the closely knit patriarchal family system of the French favors the development of identity in terms of parental figures. The difference between the French and Virgin Islanders cannot be explained simply by stating that the members of one group are more suspicious or hostile than those of the other.

Another aspect of the problem concerns the assumption that clinically differentiated categories of mental illness have separate psychodynamic mechanisms. Here one may confuse language with process. If a patient represents a problem by saying that people do not like him or that he feels he is inferior, he is regarded as insecure and suffering from low self-esteem. Under conditions of greater stress, he may express the same problems in more "concrete" and condensed symbols. He may then state that other people turn away when he walks into a room or that there seems to be an odor about him, or he may make some reference to homosexuality to indicate his feeling of low esteem. In such a situation a diagnosis of a paranoid reaction is readily made. While the language has changed, it is doubtful whether the motivational or dynamic systems have been greatly altered.

Any extensive consideration of the handling of delusions in therapeutic situations is outside the scope of this essay. It should, though, be emphasized that with psychotic patients, both in an immediate and a conceptual sense, one is dealing with language rather than with drives and impulses. Sexual delusions, for example, are not the external representations of long-repressed drives, nor are hallucinations of a child being killed a resurrection of some old sibling rivalry. The content of such delusions and hallucinations is not determined primarily by universal biological forces, but is selected in accordance with the preferred channels of relatedness in a culture. The delusional patient talks about his problems and his feelings in language that makes his experience "real." To understand the language, one must know the stress and the culture.

TABLES AND REFERENCES

Table I—Marriages Performed in the Virgin Islands; Type of Ceremony by Denomination: 1957

Denomination	Total	BOTH PARTIES NATIVE			GROOM NATIVE			BRIDE NATIVE			BOTH PARTIES NATIVE		
		Total	STC	STT	Total	STC	STT	Total	STC	STT	Total	STC	STT
Total	278	69	26	43	50	16	34	49	10	39	110	41	69
African Methodist Episcopal	4	2	2	0	1	1	0	0	0	0	1	1	0
Baptist	0	0	0	0	0	0	0	0	0	0	0	0	0
Church of God	2	0	0	0	0	0	0	0	0	0	2	0	2
Dutch Reformed	0	0	0	0	0	0	0	0	0	0	0	0	0
Episcopalian	30	12	2	10	7	1	6	4	0	4	7	4	3
Jehovah Witness	1	0	0	0	0	0	0	1	0	1	0	0	0
Jewish	1	0	0	0	1	0	1	0	0	0	0	0	0
Lutheran	21	11	3	8	0	0	0	2	1	1	8	4	4
Moravian	38	11	5	6	10	2	8	12	1	11	5	0	5
Pentecostal	0	0	0	0	0	0	0	0	0	0	0	0	0
Pilgrim Holiness	3	0	0	0	1	1	0	0	0	0	2	1	1
Roman Catholic	58	25	12	13	3	1	2	13	3	10	17	15	2
Salvation Army	0	0	0	0	0	0	0	0	0	0	0	0	0
Seventh Day Adventist	5	1	0	1	2	1	1	0	0	0	2	0	2
Spanish Methodist	2	0	0	0	1	1	0	0	0	0	1	1	0
United Brothers in Christ	2	1	1	0	1	1	0	0	0	0	0	0	0
Wesleyan Methodist	42	2	0	2	7	1	6	4	0	4	29	0	29
Civil	69	4	1	3	16	6	10	13	5	8	36	15	21

Virgin Islands

By religious ceremony	209	75.2%
By civil ceremony	69	24.8

St. Croix

By religious ceremony	66	71.0%
By civil ceremony	27	29.0

St. Thomas

By religious ceremony	143	77.3%
By civil ceremony	42	22.7

STC—St. Croix
STT—St. Thomas and St. John.

Table II—Total Live Births and Illegitimate Births, Virgin Islands and Each Island: 1930-1958

Year	VIRGIN ISLANDS Total	Illegitimate No.	Per Cent	ST. CROIX Total	Illegitimate No.	Per Cent	ST. THOMAS Total	Illegitimate No.	Per Cent	ST. JOHN Total	Illegitimate No.	Per Cent
1930	592	344	58.1	263	168	63.9	314	171	54.5	15	5	33.3
1931	478	287	60.0	210	131	62.4	257	151	58.8	11	5	45.5
1932	553	330	59.7	261	169	64.8	279	156	55.9	13	5	38.5
1933	579	361	62.3	301	194	64.5	266	163	61.3	12	4	33.3
1934	657	405	61.6	312	205	65.7	332	195	58.7	13	5	38.5
1935	657	388	59.1	334	207	62.0	304	169	55.6	19	12	63.2
1936	665	390	58.6	335	216	64.5	315	170	65.0	15	4	26.7
1937	726	423	58.3	370	236	63.8	337	178	52.8	19	9	47.4
1938	705	391	55.5	366	207	56.6	323	176	54.5	16	8	50.0
1939	787	443	56.3	381	220	57.7	389	215	55.3	17	8	47.1
1940	756	411	54.4	386	229	59.5	355	176	49.6	16	6	37.5
1941	829	461	55.4	360	222	64.4	456	230	50.4	13	9	69.2
1942	889	479	53.8	368	204	55.4	506	268	52.9	15	7	46.0
1943	931	492	52.8	344	204	59.3	572	281	49.1	15	7	46.0
1944	1080	556	51.4	410	233	56.8	655	319	47.1	15	4	26.6
1945	992	462	46.5	375	194	51.7	503	264	43.7	14	4	28.5
1946	921	441	47.9	367	262	71.3	534	222	41.5	20	7	30.5
1947	877	440	50.1	357	205	57.2	503	229	43.5	17	6	35.2
1948	829	412	49.6	320	188	58.7	497	221	44.4	12	3	25.0
1949	888	464	52.2	337	212	62.9	539	248	46.0	12	4	33.3
1950	894	448	50.1	370	229	61.9	518	217	41.9	6	2	33.3
1951	953	489	51.3	415	247	59.5	526	230	43.7	12	4	33.3
1952	862	455	52.8	387	234	60.5	461	227	49.2	14	4	28.6
1953	871	437	50.2	412	245	54.8	448	189	41.9	11	3	27.4
1954	881	426	48.4	426	245	57.5	436	175	40.1	12	6	50.0
1955	913	438	47.9	465	269	60.1	434	165	38.1	14	4	28.6
1956	971	490	50.5	457	264	57.8	497	220	44.3	17	6	35.3
1957	1039	496	47.8	485	260	53.7	534	230	43.1	20	6	30.0
1958	1122	531	47.3	487	286	58.7	613	239	39.0	22	6	27.3

Table III—Content of Delusions and Hallucinations

		Children	Religion	Obeah	Death	Violence	Sex	Color	Food	Money, Property	Institutions	Somatic
VIRGIN ISLANDERS												
St. Thomas, St. John												
Male	26	3	3	—	2	15	3	1	—	3	1	2
Female	16	9	5	3	4	6	2	—	2	2	—	2
St. Croix												
Male	10	1	1	—	—	3	1	2	3	1	1	1
Female	16	7	3	1	4	8	2	1	1	1	—	3
BRITISH VIRGIN ISLANDERS												
Tortola												
Male	5	1	2	—	—	2	1	—	—	—	—	—
Female	17	10	8	7	8	6	3	1	—	—	—	1
PUERTO RICAN												
Male	16	1	3	5	—	10	2	—	3	3	1	—
Female	6	—	—	1	1	4	2	1	4	—	—	1
FRENCH												
Male	12	—	—	2	1	4	7	1	1	2	1	1
Female	4	1	—	3	1	2	4	3	2	1	—	1
CONTINENTAL												
Male	14	2	1	—	—	5	3	3	2	5	1	1
Female	6	1	—	—	—	1	5	—	2	—	1	—
TOTAL	148	36	26	22	21	66	35	13	20	18	7	13

REFERENCES

Braithwaite, Lloyd. "Social Stratification in Trinidad," *Social and Economic Studies*, 2 (1953).

Cameron, Norman. *The Psychology of Behavior Disorders: A Bio-social Interpretation.* Boston, 1947.

——. "Perceptual Organization and Behavior Pathology," in R. R. Blake and G. V. Ramsey (eds.), *Perception, an Approach to Personality.* New York, 1951.

——. "Paranoid Conditions and Paranoia," in S. Arleti (ed.) *American Handbook of Psychiatry.* New York, 1959.

Campbell, Alfred A. "St. Thomas Negroes—A Study of Personality and Culture," *Psychological Monographs*, 55, No. 5, 1943.

Christensen, Carlo. *Peter Von Scholten.* Lemvig, Denmark, 1955.

Clarke, Edith. *My Mother Who Fathered Me.* London, 1957.

Davis, Kingsley. "The Sociology of Prostitution," *American Social Review* (1937), pp. 744-755.

Eaton, J. W., and R. J. Weil. *Culture and Mental Disorders. A Comparative Study of the Hutterites and Other Populations.* New York, 1955.

Edwards, Bryan. *The History, Civil and Commercial, of the British Colonies in the West Indies* (3rd ed. with considerable additions). 1801.

Field, M. J. "Mental Disorder in Rural Ghana," *Journal of Mental Science,* 104, No. 437 (1958), pp. 1043-1051.

Foote, Nelson. "Identification as a Basis for a Theory of Motivation," *American Social Review,* 16 (1951), pp. 14-21.

Frazier, E. Franklin. *The Negro in the United States* (Rev. ed.). New York, 1957.

Furnas, J. C. *The Road to Harper's Ferry.* New York, 1959.

Hallowell, A. Irving. "Fear and Anxiety as Cultural and Individual Variables in a Primitive Society," *Journal of Social Psychology,* 9: 25-47, 1938.

——. "Aggression in Salteaux Society," *Psychiatry,* 3: 395-407, 1940.

——. "The Social Function of Anxiety in a Primitive Society," in C. Kluckhohn and H. A. Murray (eds.), *Personal Character and Cultural Milieu.* New York, 1948.

Henriques, Fernando. "West Indian Family Organization," *American Journal of Sociology,* 45, No. 1, 1949.

——. *Family and Colour in Jamaica.* London, 1953.

Herskovits, Melville. *The Myth of the Negro Past.* New York, 1941.

Holmberg, Allan R. *Nomads of the Long Bow: The Siriono of Eastern Bolivia.* (Smithsonian Institution Publication No. 10.) Washington, D.C.: Government Printing Office, 1950.

Honigmann, John J. "Culture Patterns and Human Stress," *Psychiatry,* 13: 25-34, 1950.

Hostetler, John A. *Amish Life.* Scottsdale, Pa., 1959.

Huyzinga, Johan. *The Waning of the Middle Ages.* New York, 1954.

Jarvis, J. Antonio. *Brief History of the Virgin Islands.* St. Thomas, V.I., 1938.

——. *The Virgin Islands and Their People.* Philadelphia, 1944.

Kerr, Madeleine. *Personality and Conflict in Jamaica.* Liverpool, 1952.

Keur, D. L., and V. Rubin (eds.). "Social and Cultural Pluralism in the Caribbean," *Annals of the New York Academy of Science,* 83, Art. 5, 1960.

Klaf, F. S., and J. G. Hamilton. "Schizophrenia—A Hundred Years Ago and Today." 1961.

Kluckhohn, Clyde. "Navajo Witchcraft," *Papers of the Peabody Museum of America,* 22, No. 2. Cambridge, 1944.

Knox, John P. *A Historical Account of St. Thomas, V.I.* New York, 1952.

Larsen, Jens. *Virgin Islands Story.* Philadelphia, 1950.

Lashley, K. S. "Dynamic Processes in Perception," in J. F. Delafresnaye (ed.), *Brain Mechanisms and Consciousness.* Springfield, Ill., 1954.

Laubscher, B. J. F. *Sex, Custom, and Psychopathology.* New York, 1938.

Lee, Dorothy. *Freedom and Culture.* New York, 1959.

Levo, John. *The Romantic Isles, a Sketch of the Church in the West Indies.* London, 1938.

Lewis, M. G. *Journal of a West India Proprietor 1815–1817.*

Lindesmith, A., and A. Strauss. *Social Psychology.* New York, 1949.

Mandelbaum, D. G. (ed.). *Selected Writings of Edward Sapir.* Berkeley, 1949.

Merrill, Gordon C. *The Historical Geography of St. Kitts and Nevis, the West Indies.* Mexico, 1958.

Mills, C. W. "Situated Actions and Vocabularies of Motives," *American Social Review,* 5: 904-13, 1940.

Nadel, S. F. "Witchcraft in Four African Societies: An Essay in Comparison," *American Anthropologist,* 54: 18-29, 1952.

Opler, M. K. "Cultural Backgrounds of Mental Health," in Opler, M. K. (ed.), *Culture and Mental Health.* New York, 1959.

—— and J. L. Singer. "Ethnic Differences in Behavior and Psychopathology: Italian and Irish," *International Journal of Social Psychiatry,* 2: 11-22, 1956.

Pares, Richard. *War and Trade in the West Indies 1739–1763.* Oxford, 1936.

Parsons, Anne. Unpublished data to appear in *Psychiatry.*

Parsons, Talcott. "Age and Sex in the Social Structure of the United States." *American Social Review,* 1942, pp. 604-616.

Price, A. Grenfell. *White Settlers in the Tropics.* (American Geographical Society publication No. 23.) New York, 1939.

Proudfoot, Mary. *Britain and the United States in the Caribbean.* London, 1954.

Richards, Audrey I. *Hunger and Work in a Savage Tribe.* Glencoe, 1948.

Roberts, L. J., and R. L. Stefani. *Patterns of Living in Puerto Rican Families.* Rio Piedras, 1949.

Rottenberg, Simon. "A Note on Economic Policy in Tortola," *Caribbean Quarterly,* 3, No. 2 (1953), pp. 110-115.

Ruck, S. K. (ed.). *The West Indian Comes to England.* London, 1960.

Ruesch, J., and G. Bateson. *Communication: The Social Matrix of Society.* New York, 1951.

Sapir, Edward. *Language.* New York, 1921.

Senior, Clarence. *The Puerto Rican Migrant in St. Croix.* Rio Piedras, 1947.

Sereno, Renzo. "Magic and Social Structure in the Lesser Antilles," *Psychiatry* 11: 15-31, 1948.

Shaw, R. "The Cha Chas of St. Thomas," *Scientific Monthly,* 38: 136-145, 1934.

Sherlock, Philip. *A Short History of the West Indies.* London, 1956.

Singer, Milton B. "Shame Cultures and Guilt Cultures," in G. Piers and M. B. Singer (eds.), *Shame and Guilt.* Springfield, Ill., 1953.

Smith, Raymond. *The Negro Family in British Guiana.* London, 1956.

Stainbrook, Edward. "Psychopathology of Schizophrenia in Bahia," *American Journal of Psychiatry,* 109: 330-335. 1952.

Strauss, Anselm. *Masks and Mirrors.* New York, 1959.

Stycos, J. Mayone. *Family and Fertility in Puerto Rico.* New York, 1955.

Tannenbaum, Frank. *Slave and Citizen. The Negro in the Americas.* New York, 1947.

Udal, J. S. "Obeah in the West Indies," *Folk Lore* (Transcripts of Folk Lore Society). 26, No. 1, 255-295. London, 1915.

Weinstein, E. A. "Changes in Language Pattern as Adaptive Mechanisms," in P. H. Hoch and J. Zubin (eds.), *Psychopathology of Communication.* New York, 1958.

—— and R. L. Kahn. *Denial of Illness: Symbolic and Neurophysiological Aspects.* Springfield, Ill., 1955.

—— and R. L. Kahn. "Patterns of Sexual Behavior Following Brain Injury," *Psychiatry,* 24: 69-78, 1961.

——, R. L. Kahn, and S. Malitz. "Confabulation as a Social Process," *Psychiatry,* 19: 383-396, 1956.

——, R. L. Kahn, and G. O. Morris. "Delusions about Children Following Brain Injury," *Hillside Hospital,* 5: 290-298, 1956.

Weinstein, Helen. "The Matricentric Family in the Virgin Islands," unpublished Master's thesis.

Westergaard, Waldemar. *The Danish West Indies 1671–1917.* New York, 1917.

Whorf, B. L. *Language, Thought and Reality.* New York, 1956.

Williams, Eric. *The Negro in the Caribbean.* Washington, D.C., 1942.

———. *Capitalism and Slavery*. Chapel Hill, 1944.

Williams, Joseph J. *Psychic Phenomena of Jamaica*. New York, 1934.

Wittkower, E. D., and J. Fried. "A Cross-cultural Approach to Mental Health Problems," *American Journal of Psychiatry*, Vol. 116, pp. 423-428, 1959.

———, H. B. Murphy, J. Fried, and H. Ellenberger. "Cross-cultural Inquiry into the Symptomatology of Schizophrenia," *Annals of the American Academy of Science*, 84: 854-63, 1960.